WEIGHT LOSS PSYCHOLOGY:

THE 4-WEEK BEHAVIOR-BASED PLAN TO OVERCOME BINGE EATING AND LOSE WEIGHT PERMANENTLY

BY:
ZILKER PRESS

ISBN: 978-1-951791-63-6

Table of Contents

Introduction

This guide includes a four-week daily behavior plan to promote weight loss. The overall goal is to enable you to change your mindset and actions in order to improve your health and wellness. Small changes will be noticed throughout these four weeks. These changes promote a sustainable weight loss due to the correction of disordered eating patterns, as daily practice and effort will transform these small changes into long-term, permanent habits.

Currently, millions of adults suffer from chronic obesity-related illnesses. Common chronic illnesses are type2 diabetes, sleep apnea, high blood pressure, depression, joint issues, and polycystic ovarian syndrome. All of these illnesses are directly connected to an excessive amount of unhealthy weight.

This four-week weight loss plan will teach you how to correct unhealthy eating patterns. These patterns include overeating, comfort eating, stress eating, bingeing, and starving. Unhealthy eating habits stem from psychological trauma and dysfunction from childhood. Childhood and early adulthood trauma promote unhealthy eating attachments. Emotions coinciding with eating decisions promote a codependent relationship to flourish and destroy your health in the process.

This comprehensive four-week plan allows you to tackle and identify mental and physical barriers to your health. Daily goals and topics will allow you to achieve long-term weight loss success by transforming your life. These four weeks will enable these new daily habits to be transferred into long-term routines, which will help you to sustain your weight loss.

Week 1:

Day 1:

The first day of any commitment to change is terrifying. Feeling overwhelmed and unsure of where to start are common emotions. The first question you need to ask yourself is, why now? It is important to determine your reason for beginning this health journey. Choosing to prioritize your health needs to be your decision. No one can force you to travel on that journey. The daily work you will put into your mental and physical health will offer both challenging and rewarding results. Your weight loss journey will test your ability to remain diligent and patient while your mind and body are confronted with past and present obstacles.

There is a need for mental and physical awareness to begin your renovation. There will be roadblocks to finding balanced health, but learning new disciplines will allow your plan to remain effective and bring you success.

Your Day 1 will initiate a series of questions.

One of the questions includes why you are starting your health journey. Your reason must consist of who is benefiting from your health change and how you will achieve the best possible health outcome in this journey.

Your reason can include: improving your health, being a more active parent, or vanity. Write down your reasons and place them everywhere in order for you to be continually focused and dedicated. Write your reasons and place them on your bathroom mirror, car, fridge, phone, and desk. Whatever you decide is your reason, make it compelling so that it will stick with you for more than four weeks.

Your chances of success dramatically improve when your reason is beyond the surface level. Everyone wishes to rock a bathing suit, but if there is nothing beyond your surface reason, remaining committed will be a struggle. You have to search within your mind, heart, and soul to identify why you wish to change your current health state.

Along with your present reason for choosing health and wellness today, you will also reflect upon your past experiences with weight loss. Adults who struggle with excessive weight have tried many diets. You have learned what does and does not work with your lifestyle and preferences. For this weight loss journey to stick and make a fruitful impact, you must make changes that will match your current routine and standard of living.

Preferences include choosing your favorite meal for the day, how often do you eat, and if you eat regularly or inconsistently? What food do you enjoy, and how often do you consume this produce? By thinking about your food routine, you can understand the role that food plays in your daily life. Reflecting on your food choices makes it easier for you to understand why you make certain food choices over others.

Right from the first day of your weight loss journey, you must try to create a vision for your life after these four weeks. You have to decide on what you want your life to look like, who want to be, as well as the goals you intend to accomplish. These goals can include having a specific job, body, house, strength, happiness, etc. Your vision-board should hang in a place where you can see it every day so as for it to serve as a reminder of why you are on this journey. This is a fun project where you can create a vision of yourself without any fear of judgment.

Before beginning a specific food plan, you should schedule a meeting with your primary care physician to discuss your optimal daily caloric intake. Your doctor will discuss with you a specific weight loss goal to focus on calories. These calories will originate from clean and healthy ingredients—the less processed food, the better when it comes to changing your eating routine. Foods to incorporate are fruits, vegetables, whole grains, and healthy sources of fats and proteins.

Along with the recommended food choices, it is also advisable that you drink lots of water. Think of these four weeks as a body cleansing process where you are trying to eliminate all unnecessary additives from your diet. Removing juices, soda, and sports drinks lessens any cravings from artificial sweeteners.

Your weight loss plan encourages healthy eating as well as regular physical exercise for a well-balanced healthy life. Exercising is an essential component of any weight loss journey. The first day of your plan will include choosing the physical activity that works best with your life.

Choosing any form of exercise is preferable to none at all. Physical exercise reduces the risk of regaining weight. You should begin your activity with a low impact exercise as regular walking provides an excellent foundation for starting your exercise routine.

Walking is low stress and high-fat burning exercise that only requires walking shoes. You can incorporate fun aspects of your personality while walking by listening to a motivational podcast, your favorite music playlist, or an audiobook. Any of these can add versatility while you walk and decrease any chance of boredom.

Along with beginning regular physical activity, you will also need to track your progress. To track your progress, you can record your daily food intake and exercise. By tracking your progress, you can also monitor your movement toward your goals. Goals promote accountability and operate as personal benchmarks for personal motivation as you move closer to them.

For accurate tracking, you must remain honest while reporting your daily food and exercise habits. Honest recording allows for daily reflection on the patterns that are both positive and negative.

All of these changes are best suited when you're organized. Getting organized will help you carry out your weight loss plan. In order to be more organized, you will need to review your pantry and shelves as well as eliminate any enticing food and replenish your kitchen with healthier choices that suit your goals.

Alongside emptying your pantry, having helpful guides to move you along your weight loss journey are fitness trackers, recipe books, and a scale. All of these promote a healthy, well-balanced life.

Furthermore, you must remember not to travel on this path alone. A transformation of your life cannot survive without a supportive community. Sharing your journey with other like-minded individuals allows you to remain committed and motivated while you are adjusting to these changes.

Sharing your new life goals with family, friends, or colleagues improves your success rate tremendously. Inviting others into your personal space may appear terrifying, and an invasion of privacy, but reaching out to others increases your chances of success. Trust others with your internal struggles and personal achievements to encourage you to continue on your journey.

For the next four weeks, you will face personal disappointment and delights. Having a supportive group gives you a daily obligation to stay committed to your objective of health and wellness as you are no longer alone on your journey.

In Summation:

The first day of your weight loss plan should identify why you are beginning a new weight loss plan.

Build eating and physical activity routine that complements your lifestyle and preferences with the help of a doctor if you are not comfortable making your own choices.

Logging eating habits and choices promote accountability, and it's strongly encouraged.

Build a support network of healthy-minded individuals to keep you on track and share your goals recommended for building a community.

Day 2:

Day two of your weight loss journey examines your relationship with food. Today you will identify how you cope with stress and where diet fits in. A common struggle amongst adults is combining their emotions with eating. Many adults with weight loss difficulties have a complicated history and relationship with food. This relationship is both harmful and dysfunctional.

To help determine your relationship with food, here is a list of unhealthy relationship dynamics.

Emotional eating is when you eat to alleviate your emotions. The common emotions you experience that makes you eat emotionally is when you are stressed, sad, tired, lonely, or bored. This is a learned relationship with food that is cultivated in childhood and early adulthood as a coping mechanism. By eating when you are emotionally compromised, you escape your emotional distress.

Adults with excessive weight lack the ability to treat their emotions in a healthy way because they were not taught how to navigate uncomfortable emotions. Eating when stressed allows for a temporary escape from reality, but this creates a codependent relationship with food.

Food does not judge, and many families use it as an expression of love and care. This false narrative creates many problematic dynamics for adults because their food intake exceeds its purpose over time.

For a successful weight loss, you must reflect upon your history with food by examining your eating habits. A healthy perspective on food understands that food does not contain any emotional connections or solutions. Food cannot fill any void in your mind or heart. Food does not also offer a healthy escape from your internal stress.

Ways you can change your impulses from food are exercising, meditating, or speaking with a supportive confidant. All of these suggestions offer an alternative to food. By changing your reaction to stress, you train your mind to find other outlets to your emotions.

To combat your compromised eating habits, a new tactic to begin practicing is intuitive eating. This includes listening to your body and mind and determining when you need to eat and the adequate quantity you need to consume by recognizing physical signs of hunger. Making conscious decisions regarding food promotes a healthy relationship.

You will learn proper eating skills and discipline when it comes to eating consistently and regularly. You will also learn to trust your judgment by recognizing cues indicating your hunger level. As you grow more comfortable with your food choices, then you will notice that intuitive eating limits obsessive and destructive eating patterns through focused effort.

Changing the way you think about food also affects the way you choose when and how you eat. The term "diet" promotes adults who struggle with their weight to develop a restrictive approach. Restricting your diet can lead to unnecessary weight gain. Learning how to respond to your food choices through listening and hearing your body cues leads to better decision making.

Another positive approach to eating includes relaxed eating. This eating style occurs in a social environment where you are emotionally and physically comfortable. This style of eating incorporates listening to your hunger cues and feeding when necessary.

Eating with a relaxed mindset incorporates many intuitive skills, but your entire body is relaxed by proper listening and ceasing when satisfied. Your mindset also remains relaxed because you are not judging your food choices. Trust in yourself to limit the feelings of guilt or shame.

Another helpful approach to weight loss is having balance. Finding your balance signifies finding what lifestyle works for you. Diets are not balanced because their very nature is restrictive and encourages obsessive and anxious behavior. Denying the body of the classes of food or limiting calories is not healthy or logical. Food is not your enemy.

In addition to a balanced weight loss plan, is the increasing flexibility in your relationship with food. It is recommended to eat consistently and regularly, but do not shame yourself if you miss a meal or if by peradventure, you eat more than the required quantity. Following your eating schedule, rather than against it, will allow you to remain committed with your weight loss plan.

Another habit that you need to avoid is compulsively labeling every item of food as good or bad, clean, or junk. This promotes unrealistic standards of living, where you will develop an acrimonious relationship to. Labeling every food item creates unnecessary mental stress, which you do not need as you work on your health.

In Summation:

Day 2 consists of a deep psychological dive into your relationship with food while promoting healthy habits. This can be done on your own or with the help of a trusted professional.

Day 2 focuses specifically on how you react emotionally to food and the trauma from your past that has led you to use food as comfort.

Changing your relationship dynamic with food is a complicated exercise that requires time and attention for you to alter your emotional relationship with food. You also ought to practice on reflecting with your relationship with food without shame and judgment.

Listen and remember why you made certain choices and what skills you can learn to improve.

Day 3:

Day 3 of your weight loss plan focuses on reflecting on your view towards food. A healthy perspective on food begins with identifying your relationship to food. Many adults who struggle with excessive weight and disordered eating use food as emotional support. This transference is learned in childhood or young adulthood as a way of dealing with emotions.

When you were younger, I believe that food provided safety and comfort, but that doesn't mean that it is the required skill or avenue in navigating negative emotions. Food is a temporary fix but creates long term codependency that often leads to obesity.

Day 3 focuses on developing healthy eating perspectives, habits, and skills. Most adults who have an unhealthy weight have lost their ability to distinguish between hunger signs. Physical hunger provides cues when you are hungry.

This is because you have attempted many diets in the past, and you have now developed a fear of failure. Due to your previous failings with incorporating a healthy balanced diet, feelings of guilt and shame naturally increase and create barriers mentally and physically. These feelings undoubtedly impact your perception of what normal eating is.

Unconventional food choices sabotage your diet. Eating chocolate chip cookies, ice cream, or fried chicken right before bed is an example of unhealthy eating habits. With your new weight loss plan, you will be able to reflect and evaluate your food choices through food tracking. Tracking your choices allows you to understand and notice any patterns that are detrimental to your weight loss.

Learning how to eat normally starts with having a reliable food journal. Your journal is an accurate representation of your choices when used correctly. Hiding your food choices simply proves that you have guilt and shame with your choices of food.

With this weight loss plan, the goal will be learning how to eat and exercise regularly and healthily. Yo-yo dieting does not provide a healthy relationship with food. Dieting is restrictive and does not allow for long term success due to the high standards that cannot be met over time.

Another sign to know if you do not have a normal eating situation is using food as an addiction. This occurs when your compulsion to eat is similar to a gambler or alcoholic. The difference between other addictions and food addictions is that you cannot ever stop eating. You can quit drinking alcohol and gambling, but you cannot quit eating. So, in order to remain healthy, you must eat safely and regularly.

Some useful coping strategies to promote a healthier relationship with food are limiting your bad food choices. This means eating desserts for only special occasions such as a birthday or holiday. Therefore, you are not making a habit of eating brownies or cheesecake regularly.

Another coping tool is to maintain flexibility when eating healthy foods. Instead of eliminating a particular food, you can simply take it once a week; you can have a modestly sized portion of a cookie for a treat. You can also allow yourself a small slice of chocolate on Saturday as a reward for all of your hard work.

Another skill to promote a healthy eating routine is journaling your food intake. Documenting your eating habits and emotions help indicate patterns. You may start to notice when you slip away from good eating habits by consuming chips, cookies, or other junk food when you are feeling sad, anxious, or depressed.

Another helpful tip is that instead of having an unhealthy snack when you're bored or upset, you should try going for a short walk or do some deep breathing exercises. These promote exercising and meditating instead of eating, thus transforming unhealthy habits into healthy solutions.

Other behavioral changes that need to be incorporated are deep breathing, meditation, yoga, and cardio exercise. These habits allow you to stop your mind from spiraling and move slowly in a more neutral direction.

Other behavioral changes include eating healthier snacks, vegetables, fruits, nuts, popcorn as healthy alternatives to sugary desserts or salty snacks.

Changing how you think about food allows you to react differently to your food choices.

As your life is growing and evolving during this four-week weight loss journey, you also have to increase your success by learning how to cook. Instead of heating up a meal in the microwave or picking up food from a deli or fast food joint, you can learn to cook new meals.

Cooking doesn't have to be overly complicated; you can simply buy a steamer and throw vegetables in it or use an indoor grill.

These skills can work as mindfulness exercises in patience and appreciation for your food. By preparing for your food, you are developing a newfound appreciation for the effort you are putting into your food. The process of food preparation is a newfound skill that works well with this process.

In Summation:

Day 3 consists of identifying your specific view of food. This includes how and why you eat. Examining your food history allows you to reflect on its production.

A great starting point is developing healthier food habits to train your brain to react differently when you are emotionally compromised.

Healthy food habits include eating a healthy breakfast. Starting your day off with a hearty and protein-infused meal helps control hunger and increase your energy throughout the day.

Other habits are eating three meals a day with a healthy protein to prevent hunger throughout the day. Other habits are that you have to learn to eat slowly and always endeavor to drink water before each meal.

It is also recommended to have a healthy sleep routine, which promotes weight loss.

Lastly, by refusing to relate food to emotional support, liberates your mind and body from depending on food.

Day 4:

Your goal for Day 4 is to develop the right tools to increase awareness of your food habits and to incorporate a healthy weight loss routine. A treatment for food addiction is known as cognitive-behavioral therapy.

Cognitive-behavioral therapy is a widely accepted and used treatment for adults who suffer from excessive weight-related complications. This form of therapy examines your relationship with food consciously and subconsciously.

This form of therapy examines your relationship with food. The therapist guides you in recording the thoughts and feelings you experience before, during, and after a bingeing episode. Analyzing the thoughts and feelings you have towards food helps reveal the underlying reason for your addiction.

With CBT, you are able to improve your self-confidence. Adults who suffer from excessive weight usually have a poor body image that is emphasized with negative thoughts. CBT tracks your thoughts and the reasons.

Self-confidence improves with individual therapy sessions. A reoccurring emotion that most adults face is disappointment in themselves and others. CBT therapy teaches you the skills that improve your responses to perceived negativity and increase your resilience. By changing your perspective on others' actions and behaviors, you will naturally increase your self-esteem.

Your relationship with food will naturally improve as your mental health improves as there are related to one another. Ways to improve your self-esteem include positive self-talk, having a strong support system, and exercise.

Improving your self-esteem relies on changing your eating patterns. By increasing your tolerance to negativity, you will have to refrain from bingeing and snacking on harmful foods. Over time, your foods will be more nutritious because you will no longer crave sugary or savory food items that promote weight gain.

To implement the tools provided in CBT, you must try to pause before and while you're eating. By doing so, you will be able to take a moment to check your emotional state. Ask yourself if you are actually physically hungry or psychologically hungry. Psychological hunger appears identical to feelings of anger, sadness, loneliness, and boredom. Pausing and taking the time to put your thoughts together is a great starting point in identifying and breaking your eating cycle.

Another way in which CBT can impact your eating habits is through learning how to be comfortable in your body. Many adults turn to food when they are uncomfortable. With CBT, you learn how to accept discomfort, accept food cravings, and remain dedicated to your food plan.

Along with your CBT sessions, you can also practice your positive thinking by changing your perspective towards food. Viewing food as nutrition and as a form of energy encourages more healthy behavior.

One habit of relinquishing is impulsive dieting. Bingeing increases your body weight. Drastically cutting calories or not eating certain kinds of food leads to overeating and makes it more difficult to recover from the disorder.

Another habit in which you need to train your mind is distinguishing between a snack and a treat. Snacking is a smart way of making sure that you are not ravenous when dinnertime arrives. By letting yourself become so hungry, you're likely going to overeat on foods that you should only eat in moderation. By choosing to snack, you must also remember to choose a healthy snack.

A treat is for pure enjoyment, while a snack is something you eat between meals to stave off hunger. Examples of healthy snack options are nuts, fruit, or cheese, but not chocolate.

Another habit you ought to instill in yourself is making regular meals a habit. By skipping meals, you increase your chances of overeating because you will be very hungry. You will also likely be eating food that is high in fat and sugar, which are often ingredients that trigger a binge.

By eating daily meals regularly, you will be able to prevent increased all-day hunger. You should also try to choose healthy foods for your meals and snacks. These food choices offer plenty of nutrients, lower your cravings, and lessen the change to overeat.

The meal that is most important for substantial weight loss is eating breakfast regularly. Eating a healthy breakfast provides more energy, memories, and lowers cholesterol throughout your day. Starting your day off with a healthy, balanced breakfast with proteins, fats, and carbs and not high in sugar is key to healthy eating.

Another helpful habit is keeping your cravings out of sight. This is prevented by not having foods high in sugar or fat. If you are recovering from food addiction, you should try to keep less food in your home; even those food that tends to be healthy. This is because bingeing is normally in private, so you have to keep only as much food as you need for a short time. This gives you less of a chance to binge.

Along with therapy, you also need to spend time with friends and family who are healthy eaters. Do not fall into the trap of eating alone because you will be more likely to binge. You should also try to avoid people who make negative comments about your weight or eating habits.

Through these four weeks, you will essentially be learning how to eat again. Learning that which is the correct and healthy way to eat. Instead of looking at food as a chore or burden, take the time to value your relationship with food as you become more comfortable.

Admit that it is important to sit down and eat while cherishing your mealtime.

Another helpful tip is allowing yourself to feel hungry by observing your body's instinctual cues for hunger.

This may seem overwhelming because of the many considerations you need to have when eating, but keeping a balanced approach is key for long term success.

Do not become overly strict and rigid. Life is meant to be experienced.

In Summation:

Day 4 tackles the inclusion of Cognitive Behavioral Therapy as a tool to treat your disordered eating. Weight loss is mental in developing a healthy dynamic with food.

CBT teaches you many solutions in navigating your emotions. It also improves your self-esteem and offers alternatives to unhealthy food choices.

CBT is also effective when you improve your eating skills through mindfulness techniques. These techniques include pausing and appreciating the food you have prepared to inject.

Day 5:

Day 5 focuses on the power of auto-suggestion. Autosuggestion is a mind technique where your conscious thoughts lead to unconscious actions. Adults typically use auto-suggestion unconsciously. Training your mind to harness its positive thoughts, feelings, and beliefs actively promotes weight loss. Your weight loss will naturally occur through the presence of positive thinking, which improves your self-esteem organically.

Self-esteem and positive thinking are intrinsically related because the power of your mind also controls your behavior. Positive thinking promotes positive actions, and the reversed is true. Adults with excessive weight problems have low self-esteem, which stems from a low opinion of their body because their mind believes it to be true.

There is also the need for you to reframe your internal messages. With adequate time and practice, you will be able to master the art of not judging yourself after eating certain foods. You will also need to do some exercises to remind you, during meals, that food benefits you specifically at that time. Reminding yourself of the benefits of food can help make your meals move from being strictly negative into a more positive space.

"Think about how whatever it is you're eating is going to give you the energy to do what you love in the world and help others."

You will also need to include daily affirmations or positive statements as they naturally improve and promotes weight loss. This is because you will begin to believe that what you are saying is true and real. Poor opinions of you are roadblocks to long term weight loss success. If you believe that you are either ugly, that you have no significance, and that you are likely to fail, you will inevitably confirm your beliefs through your actions.

Daily affirmations improve your resiliency to obstacles you will encounter throughout your weight loss journey. Mental barriers include negative self-talk that are often disparaging and not helpful. Having a strong mind improves your chances of overcoming negative thoughts and beliefs.

Powerful affirmations you can use include:

"Every day, in every way, I am becoming a better me."

"I am discovering delicious new foods that make me healthier."

"I am proud of myself for choosing a healthier lifestyle."

"I am giving myself the strong, healthy body I deserve."

When you use empowering statements, your subconscious mind eventually accepts them as fact, making your reality stronger and more productive.

Along with positive affirmations towards food, you also need to acknowledge your life outside of the food you choose by thinking of food in the taste of what you are consuming and who you are sharing it with. By enjoying the joy of eating, or the meal you share, you can bring not only nutrients but happiness and memories along with it.

To remove guilt or regret after a meal, pause and check within your emotions before you spiral. Take in your feelings by observing outside your body, which is free from judgment. If you feel guilty about an unhealthy choice of food, you should observe and reflect on why you made that choice and what you could do in the future to prevent that behavior from occurring. This may have happened due to a light lunch or dinner that led to you snacking late at night.

By observing your actions without judgment, you will begin to notice patterns that are more helpful than simply judging what you have done in the past. Learn from your actions and make different choices in the future. You will also save time and energy by not attacking yourself.

Along with observing your behaviors and increasing positive thoughts, you can also try to shift your view on food. By focusing on the nourishment that food provides, your view on food can improve. Food has the ability to heal you from ailments and prevent future illnesses.

Wild proteins, natural fats, and leafy greens help heal injuries, grow healthy hair, and build strong muscles. By choosing healthier foods, you are able to sleep soundly, feel vibrant, and escape food-related illnesses.

Instead of choosing food that will harm you immediately or later, choosing the food that heals will allow your mind and body to thrive.

By affirming that you are only human, your happiness and health are intertwined with your health when it is in balance. With the intentional choices that positively direct your life, your body can grow and change.

Foods that increase mental positivity are eggs, kombucha, mushrooms, whole grains, and chocolate.

Eggs are great for increasing mental agility because of their high-quality proteins and mood-boosting B vitamins. Eggs increase healthy cholesterol that leads to a better, balanced mood.

Kombucha and chocolate are great for mental health that proactively prevent and protect against depression.

Whole grains are recommended instead of refined grains because they lower the rates of depression. Mushrooms also increase serotonin and decrease depressive episodes. Mushrooms are one of the only sources of vitamin D that is essential to your mental health.

In Summation:

Day 5 tackles the idea of positive thoughts working through your mind into your present state. Autosuggestion improves your mental health by increasing your self-esteem, which are common areas adults with excessive weight struggle with.

Improving your self-confidence increases your chance of sustained weight loss because you have the mental strength and confidence to combat barriers to your physical health and wellness.

You can never say enough positive statements about your choices. By having healthier food options, you will develop stronger taste buds for a variety of foods.

Day 6:

Day 6 of your weight loss journey focuses on setting attainable and realistic goals. These goals should focus on your eating habits and begin an organized food plan. Your goals for weight loss can either highlight specific outcomes or overall process.

An outcome goal is what you hope to achieve at the end, which can be losing a certain amount of weight. This is a target, but you need benchmarks to hit along the way as you proceed to your end goal. Process goals help to determine how to change your daily behavioral habits that promote your overall long-term goal.

To help in achieving your major goal of sustained large weight loss, you need to set yourself up for success with a set of mini-goals. These goals should be more attainable when even a modest weight loss can improve your blood pressure, cholesterol, blood sugar, and triglyceride levels. Losing as little as ten pounds can positively change many chemicals in your body.

You can experience incredible progress in weight loss by having mini goals toward reaching your ultimate goal, and that can be achieved within a month. Tracking your progress and rewarding yourself along the way by improving eating and exercise habits. Examples of such habits might be by going to the gym five times a week, treat yourself to flowers, a movie, or a football game, whichever feels like a reward to you. This maintains your positive attitude and reminds you of the benefits of a healthier lifestyle.

In addition to having mini-goals, you can also adopt changes that are easy to maintain. These can include leaving small bites of food on each place, slowing down and tasting every bite, eliminating interruptions to your meals, filling spare time with activities instead of eating, etc.

Better behaviors include walking 5,000 steps per day, switching to light food products, giving up fried foods, starting each day with a nutritious breakfast. These changes must be easy for you to incorporate into your life, and with daily repetition, they will become part of your life.

An example of a process goal is to eat a serving of protein at every meal, walk thirty minutes a day, or drink water thirty minutes before your meal. With a healthy food foundation, your next step for your weight loss goal is to organize your food plan. Your food plan for weight loss promotion should include a high protein breakfast, which will reduce your cravings and calorie intake throughout the day.

Another tip is avoiding any sugary drinks and fruit juice. These drinks are fattening and are not recommended for your weight loss. Another suggestion for your weight loss plan consists of drinking water before meals, which will increase your weight loss.

Food plans with maximum success should include regular amounts of protein. Protein is a vital nutrient that boosts your metabolism, reduces your appetite, and helps regulate your hunger hormones. Optimum ways to receive more protein for your diet are optimal protein-rich foods, which include: Meats, fish, eggs, dairy, and legumes.

Healthy meat options include chicken, turkey, lean beef, and pork. Healthy fish consists of salmon, sardines, haddock, and trout.

Healthy dairy contains milk, cheese, and yogurt. Healthy legumes include kidney beans, chickpeas, and lentils.

By eating fresh and unpackaged food, you are decreasing your sodium, fat, and sugar content exclusively. Limiting these ingredients increases your weight loss. Replace your packaged snack with healthier foods such as baby carrots, hummus, Greek yogurt, and fresh berries, natural peanut butter with an apple. All these are healthy alternatives that will reward your body for your continued dedication.

Another goal you need to incorporate is for you to use the stairs whenever possible. Adding two to three minutes of stair climbing per day burns enough calories to eliminate one to two pounds of weight gain. With that, you are not only burning calories but also strengthening your glutes and quad muscles.

You can also improve your health by preparing your lunch. You not only save on calories but also on hundreds of dollars. Sodium and calories are significantly reduced because of the fresh ingredients. You are also in control of the portion and quality of the food used. You are reducing sugar, salt, and fat, which are typically higher in a restaurant.

Alongside your health-related goals, it is also important to have non-weight loss goals. These goals are easier to maintain motivation on a long-term basis such as: improving sleep, improving posture, increasing strength, building better confidence and self-esteem.

In Summation:

Day 6 should focus on healthy and organized eating habits. Recommended eating habits include eating slowly and intentionally with a protein-focused diet.   Healthy protein helps curb hunger cravings and promote weight loss.

Another helpful tip is regular and consistent sleep.   Without adequate sleep, you increase the risk of gaining weight.

Day 7:

Day 7 deals with obsessing over the scale. This will deal with common traps of obsessing over numbers as you begin your weight loss journey. Focusing on the process of exercise rather than the outcome leads to greater overall success with your weight loss journey.

When adults have suffered from failed diet and exercise routines continuously, they will feel the excitement and jubilation at their initial weight loss success, but over time, weight loss decreases.

You may need to adjust your weight loss priorities if you are obsessing over specific aspects of your weight loss routine. Signs you are obsessing over your weight includes, cutting out entire food groups due to a fear of potential weight gain with no actual evidence to support your theory.

Another sign of potentially unhealthy habits is eating only at certain times, which can lead to a feeling of hunger and depriving your body of essential nutrients. By having a rigid eating schedule, your risk of overeating at your next meal increases if your body interprets these eating habits as you starving yourself. Allowing flexibility to eat reduces feelings of hunger when healthy food is eaten continuously where all nutrients are accessible.

Another sign you are having difficulty with your new weight loss plan is avoiding restaurants due to anxiety. When you lose control over meal preparation, fear of possible overeating is plausible and understandable. Still, when it prevents you from socializing, new experiences indicate that you have a slight problem. Other signs of obsession are unhealthy exercise routines that merge with obsession. Forgiving yourself when conflicts in life occur is essential for long-term weight loss success.

The most common sign of anxiety and obsession directly relate to the scale. If you constantly weigh yourself multiple times a day, this indicates you suffer from an unrealistic mentality towards weight loss. Weight naturally fluctuates throughout the day, and changes in one to two pounds are completely acceptable and normal.

Stepping on the scale to monitor your weight loss and stay on track is completely reasonable. Healthy weight routines can either be in the morning when you first wake up or weekly.

A Summation:

Obsessing over numbers is never a good habit to begin any weight loss journey. Numbers are helpful when accessing progress and remaining on track, but checking your weight multiple times a day is unhealthy and obsessive.

Adults with an excessive weight with failed weight loss experience can obsess over their success through the use of monitoring numbers. Weight loss success is not measured by numbers only. Changing your perspective to include non-number achievements will aid in your long-term weight loss success.

Some non-scale victories include visual changes. You can take a picture of yourself wearing the same outfit weeks apart and notice a visual difference. This provides an incentive to continue with your changes. Other victories include healthy changes to your skin, which may become less oily and have fewer acne breakouts as your diet changes. By living a healthier lifestyle, your sleep will also drastically improve.

Week 2:

Day 8:

Congratulations on beginning the second week of your weight loss plan. Day 8 focuses on tracking your daily routine. This includes food intake, exercise, emotional states, and relevant notes. By journaling your daily food, exercise, and mood routines, you will be able to track the patterns you exhibit, as well as your response. By recording your portion sizes, caloric intake, and food groups, you will also be able to notice positive and negative patterns that need adjusting and improvement.

Due to the correlation between mood and food consumption, journaling any episodes of emotional upheaval helps with overcoming any barriers to your health. Your journaling experience will be successful as long as you take it seriously and honestly.

Along with food consumption struggles, many adults who struggle with their weight avoid the scale. Viewing the scale as the only self-identifier to your worth is counterproductive to weight loss. A balanced food intake with fresh ingredients will be reflected by the number on the scale but is not the only factor you need to consider. To become more comfortable with weighing yourself regularly, you need to begin or continue journaling to acknowledge and observe your eating habits.

Eating habits are critical in their reflection of your weight. Having a healthy approach to weight loss is critical; therefore, not obsessing over the number on the scale is important. Obsessive thinking over the number on the scale is a damaging mindset to adopt.

Forcing yourself to remove any connection between the number on the scale and your overall identity is necessary to have. Your entire self-worth does not start or end with the number on the scale.

The scale offers a tool for measuring your weight and identifying whether or not your weight loss habits are working correctly.

Another healthy skill to adopt is logging your food intake immediately after you eat. Waiting until the end of the day increases the odds of forgetting what you drank and ate for that day. Do not trust your memory for accurate food details.

Another tip for successful food tracking is to include all food ingredients, such as butter or oil, in your journal. Measuring your portions is also recommended because underreporting your portion sizes might lead to overeating and increasing calories unnecessarily. In order to help with portion control, it is important to use measuring cups and spoons to prevent unneeded calorie intake.

A healthy relationship with food starts with viewing food as a daily necessity to function, and not as an enemy to your success. Adults who have battled with their weight for years often start obsessing over calories. Your focus should be on the nutritional value of your food. Valuing fat, carbs, and protein content in your food promotes weight loss. Nutritional food increases your intake variety and optimal health.

Another helpful skill is recording whenever you're eating your meals. For your food journal, recording when you eat determines the length of time between meals and analyzing reasons for possible overeating. Overeating usually occurs when there are long gaps between meals. The opposite is also true if you eat too often when you're not really hungry, it leads to overeating as well.

The added benefit of recording your food intake is analyzing the relationship between your food choices with your current state of mind. Journaling your moods alongside your meals, exposes your emotional eating patterns. You can ask yourself questions to determine your state of mind, and such questions include:

"Am I hungry?"

"Am I anxious?"

"Am I lonely?"

"Am I tired?"

"Am I eating out of habit instead of hunger?

If any of these answers include an emotion, you can then conclude that your emotional state is tied deeply to food. You must learn to nurture your emotions without food and adopt other habits to focus your energy on.

Helpful weight loss apps that are strongly recommended for a healthy balanced life include: Lose It!, Noom, Daily Burn, Fitbit, Health/Out, Cron-O-Meter, Fooducate, and Eat This, Not That! The Game, etc. All of these apps can make tracking your health goals easier and less stressful.

According to experts, the best overall app for tracking weight loss is, Lose It! This app compiles your daily food diary into daily and weekly into reports. The overall tracker for this app is calories. You will be able to set goals and ask questions about your current weight.

This app is useful for your overall weight loss because all of the pressure of counting calories is shared with this app. You can also monitor your progress regularly, which makes it easier to remain committed to your goals.

There is also a customized weight loss plan for you to follow, which increases your chances of success. There are also food recommendations to coincide with your goals. Extra assistance and guidance in food planning enable you to expand your culinary palette and learn new cooking techniques. This time will be a time to learn and expand your food skills and knowledge.

There are three methods to track your food. The first method includes scanning the barcode of your packaged food or taking a photo of your food. This form of tracking provides accurate data in knowing your weight loss trajectory. This accurate food tracking allows you to have detailed descriptions of the food you are consuming and helps in identifying any unhealthy patterns. There are also foods to avoid due to their unhealthy nutritional value.

Another helpful weight loss tracking app is Noom. This app focuses on having the ability to eat any food. Through a nonrestrictive eating model, you are able to meet your weight loss goals through a balanced approach and mindset.

Many adults with excessive weight find weight-loss programs tedious and hard to maintain. Having a structured supporting network increases your chances of changing your lifestyle. The Noom app integrates psychology to combine both physical and mental habits for weight loss. Having a well-balanced approach to weight loss by tackling both physical and mental health allows for healthy habits to be nurtured long term.

The overall goal of Noom is changing eating habits through supportive health coaches that provide useful information and tools to start and maintain a healthy, balanced life. Understanding the value of integrative health is critical to your weight loss journey. Weight loss is often an attack on your will power and can be mentally exhausting. Having a supportive app that can guide you through your struggles is necessary and useful.

Another app that is highly regarded for weight loss is Daily Burn. Daily burn is an exercise-based app that allows you to choose group classes or individual sessions of various exercise routines to increase your physicality. This app offers fun and supportive techniques in promoting a healthy exercise routine.

Often, along with a healthy diet, a regular exercise routine can become stale and boring, but with this app, you are able to diversify your exercise and try new classes. By building and strengthening your endurance and flexibility, you will carefully cultivate a great workout regimen.

Common exercises this app has include yoga classes, running classes, circuit training workouts, and high-intensity interval training. Along with the wide variety of workout classes, there are various exercises that you can follow virtually on any device.

This app is valuable for accommodating your busy adult life. This app's goal is to be able to fit in with your lifestyle and habits. Due to the widespread nature of technology, you will be able to find an exercise routine that meets your goals and standards quickly and efficiently.

A summation:

Food journaling is a helpful skill to have throughout the stages of your weight loss journey as you are still learning new eating habits and adjusting to a new routine. Recording your portions, length of time between meals, and emotional state while eating are incredibly useful to promote a healthy weight loss.

If you are unsure about portion sizes, having cups and spoons in your vicinity will improve the sizing of your food choices.

Having a mental check-in while eating is also essential in determining why you are eating. Noticing a pattern is the first step in treating your emotional eating.

There is a wide variety of tracking apps that aid in meeting your weight loss goals. There are a variety of apps that specialize in specific areas from physical support, mental support, or basic calorie counting. All apps will improve your ability to track your progress as long as you remain diligent and focused.

Day 9:

Day 9 highlights the social changes happening in your life as you adjust to a healthy lifestyle. Due to your health changes, you will naturally attract both mentally and physically different people. Your relationships will also shift in a more positive and, unfortunately, negative direction.

Your values are evolving due to shifting your personal goals, which affects every social aspect of your life. The shifts affect family, friends, colleagues, and potential romantic interests. The relationships will be tested, changed, and altered due to the changes you are utilizing in your own life.

Every small change creates a ripple effect. Your ripple effect may take many different forms. You will notice small modifications in your relationships, but most of all, you will notice your need for positive support throughout your journey.

The main change in your relationships will be adapting to extra attention as your appearance changes. Friends, family members, co-workers, and peers will give you more attention after you lose weight. This extra attention will feel odd and make you feel uncomfortable, flattered, resentful, or self-conscious. Any change in your interactions with strangers will be exciting, new, and unusual. It is best to maintain a positive outlook and learn about your reactions to every situation.

Be patient with yourself and others as you adjust to your changing body and give them the time to also adjust. Some are going to adjust positively, while others are going to have to work through their jealousy.

Along with an increase in attention, there will be possible negative side effects as well. Your relationships may experience envy for the first time as your weight loss changes the dynamics. As you lose weight, you will naturally gain more self-confidence, which may lead others to feel insecure in comparison. This change to your dynamic will create conflict and jealousy.

Often, when you lose weight, others feel the need to offer their opinion and inject their own experience and advice. This behavior is typically never encouraged, but adults, on average, see your changes as a reflection on their health state, which is never your intention. Unfortunately, most adults view your weight loss as an opportunity for them to express their thoughts and opinions. This will make you feel frustrated, but maintaining an air of neutrality is recommended as you continue on your health journey.

Along with jealousy, family members may become unsupportive by monitoring or policing your food intake. This form of behavior may appear complementary, but it is another form of controlling your behavior. By controlling your behavior, your family is negatively responding to your positive health choices.

To counteract negative behaviors from family members, you can organize activities that do not have food as the focus point. Along with changing social gatherings, you can also incorporate more healthy options by serving vegetables, going for a long walk, or dining in instead of going to a restaurant. Other supportive gestures to include family members are inviting them to a support group meeting or counseling session. All of these are positive alternatives to enduring constant judgment and ridicule at food-focused family get-togethers.

Many aspects of your social life will be challenged as you mature and develop this new facet of your life. For example, in many social situations, the theme revolves around food and drinking. During your weight loss journey, discovering new ways to enjoy yourself that do not revolve around drinking and eating is a great step towards minimizing your anxiety.

Anxiety over missing out on your social life is expected and natural during these weeks of change and growth. You are challenging your routine and comfort zone, so naturally, there will be resistance from yourself and others.

To help prevent unnecessary stress as you exercise more and improve your eating habits, you will need to integrate emotional and practical support systems into your life. Emotional support includes having a close friend or family member who you can share your thoughts and feelings with, whether they are positive or negative. Sharing your journey allows you to recommit to your goal and maintain accountability because you are not alone.

Practical support includes having someone who understands your goals and values with unconditional support. This can occur when you choose to exercise and need someone to run an errand for you or watch your children. This person understands your actions without judgment and only wants to help and aid in your growth and progress.

Lastly, having inspirational support is vital to curb any anxiety during this transitional period. Inspiration support can come from a professional or an active partner in your weight loss journey. You can turn to a counselor to share your thoughts and feelings during your journey, or to a personal trainer and exercise partner. Getting someone to cheer you up on the sidelines or next to you gives you the right motivation.

Unfortunately, some people in your social circles will not be supportive of your health changes. They will respond negatively and judgmentally, and it is your choice to continue the relationship or not.

Building a strong community of support lessens your anxiety to your changing life. Change is often difficult and met with resistance. There will be many people in your circle of friends and family that will show unsupportive behaviors.

An app that helps with building your new and expanding social life is HealthyOut. This app will lessen your anxiety surrounding eating out in a social setting. As you gain confidence in your weight loss habits, you can begin to participate in social events that include food.

It is best to start small and prepare ahead physically and mentally to prevent stress and anxiety. The HealthyOut app helps ease your worry regarding dining out with its many healthy options. You can filter out food based on calorie counts, which makes the overall dining out experience more enjoyable and effective.

Eating out can appear tricky because of potential weird looks from friends and staff with your special requests or questions. Still, this app will do most of that work for you beforehand to decrease any uncomfortable or unknowns as you prepare for your dining out experience.

Being prepared for the mental, emotional, and social changes that accompany weight loss will help you achieve your goal of overall health and well-being. Try to practice forgiveness with yourself and others because this is a learning period where your boundaries are shifting, and they will choose if they are able to adjust or not.

A Summation:

Helpful ways to create a support network is staying in touch with friends and family through phone calls, emails, and texts when you feel down. Also, finding a supportive partner that you can walk with, plan a fun outing, and cook healthy meals will decrease anxiety and stress over social situations.

Another helpful way to incorporate your healthy goals and values is joining in with community organizations, local exercise classes, or neighborhood events that can broaden your social group with likeminded individuals.

There is a helpful dining out app that has suggestions in navigating dining out experiences. These suggestions include calorie count, specific food preferences such as Italian or Mexican, and specific dietary restrictions like vegan, Paleolithic or Ketogenic diets.

As your social life expands, it may also need to shrink as well. Certain relationships are forever altered due to your change in lifestyle habits. Many will have support for your changes, while others will feel that your changes are a reflection upon them, and they will react with anger and jealousy.

Make choices in your relationships that will properly support you. Put your needs first.

Day 10:

Day 10 highlights the difference between psychological hunger and physical hunger. These are two distinctly different eating impulses and experiences.

Lacking the ability to determine your signals for fullness is a primary reason for your struggles with weight. Your body naturally tells you when you are full and hungry, but if you have not listened to these signals for years or decades, you need to reset your mind and body. These signals are still there, but you are out of practice.

Psychological hunger is not an actual impulse for food. This form of hunger is caused by a desire to eat out of habit or being emotionally compromised. Eating out of habit happens when you see food around you or consume food because it seems like a good idea.

An example of psychological hunger is eating dessert at the end of your meal, even when you are not hungry for dessert. You are choosing to eat dessert because of the habit fostered through previous eating experiences that have been socially acceptable regardless of actual hunger.

On your weight loss journey, recognizing your physical hunger from psychological hunger is crucial. Physical hunger includes possible rumbling sensation in your stomach, which weakens your stamina over time. Also, with physical hunger, you will have emptiness in your stomach that proves you are hungry. Psychological hunger does not provoke any physical symptoms of hunger; it is only in your mind.

To help determine what your signals are, you need to journal and track your eating patterns. For two weeks or longer, write down not only when and what you eat but also what you are doing and feeling before you start eating. Journaling what you eat allows a pattern to emerge for most adults who are struggling with their weight.

An example of a negative eating pattern is always eating dinner in front of the television. Another negative habit is always having an evening snack, even when you are not hungry. This evening snack occurs even when you feel like you want to eat, but you are not truly hungry.

The desire to eat is a habit that has been cultivated over years of routines. Your weight loss journey includes learning your hunger signs, listening to them, and not overindulging. Stopping when you are actually full includes listening to your body and breathing slowly while you eat.

A way to help identify your hunger cues is by using the hunger scale. This tool helps you differentiate between physical hunger and psychological hunger; when the hunger is just in your head. This scale ranges from a 1, which means you are starving, and a 10, meaning you are so full that you feel sick. A 5 or 6 means you are comfortable; you are neither hungry nor full.

The full Hunger scale includes:

1. Indicates starving, weakness or dizziness

2. Indicates very hungry, cranky, low energy or stomach growling

3. Indicates hunger or stomach is growling a little

4. Indicates starting to feel a little hungry

5. Indicates satisfied or neither hungry nor full

6. Indicates a little full or pleasantly full

7. Indicates a little uncomfortable

8. Indicates feeling stuffed

9. Indicates very uncomfortable or stomach hurts

10. Indicates so full you feel sick

Adults who struggle with too much weight, typically lack the skill of proper eating because they were never taught, thus increasing their negative eating habits over time. By journalizing your daily intake of food, you can recognize your emotional states when eating. There is usually an eating pattern that indicates psychological hunger.

To prevent a hunger scale of a 1 or 2, you need to eat when your hunger is at a 3 or 4. Do not wait until your stomach is growling, or you are in physical pain. Becoming so ravenous that you overeat is not a healthy habit to continue when learning how to eat healthily. When you sit down for a scheduled meal, you should reflect and think about how hungry you are. Listen to your current physical state and monitor your body's reactions as you eat.

With more practice and reflection, you will gain experience by eating more or less food so that you can finish eating regularly until you reach a comfortable 5 or 6 feeling. Your goal should be neutral or content after eating. Anything on either end of the spectrum is not recommended before or after eating.

To promote a healthier eating routine and combat your psychological hunger incorporating more protein, carbohydrates, and fiber in your diet lessens cravings and increases fullness throughout your day. Healthy carbohydrates include grains, fruits, and vegetables. Healthy proteins include meat, fish, eggs, milk, yogurt, cheese, dry beans, and nuts, while healthy fats include fish, walnuts, flaxseeds, olive, canola, most nuts, avocados, and peanut oils.

Another tool to combat psychological hunger is incorporating mindfulness techniques while eating. Mindfulness occurs when you are aware of what you are feeling physically and mentally from moment to moment.

Eating mindfully begins by taking slow breaths before eating. Then, you begin breathing from your abdomen rather than your chest. Observe your plate of food and decide whether it is balanced. Lastly, pause while you eat to taste the food as you slow down your eating process.

Mindful eating increases your chance of enjoying this experience and valuing your food. You will want to savor the taste and feeling of nourishing your body. When you rush the experience, you do not have the time or ability to notice your senses and experience.

With practice, you will learn to stop eating when you are full and not when you feel stuffed. Eating until you are too full is not a habit you want to continue because overeating prevents progress with weight loss.

To prevent overeating, you can also incorporate a more relaxed mindset by slowly eating and chewing your food. Notice the flavors and textures of each bite of food and listen to how your body responds. Checking in with your senses helps to learn specific sensations and cues your body gives out. Never feel obligated to finish your plate of food; your needs come before the food.

Along with mindful eating habits, you also need to measure and learn proper portions. Restaurant portions are typically too large for a size you should be ingesting. Smaller portions promote healthy eating habits where you do not feel stressed and obligated to finish your plate of food.

In Summation:

Day 10 focuses on developing your ability to differentiate between eating out of habit versus an actual physical hunger. This is a skill that requires time to develop. Keeping a journal to monitor your portion sizes, mood patterns, and food choices help identify cravings as you change your diet habits.

Eating mindfully is a recommended skill to promote healthy eating habits and food enjoyment. Mindful eating skills increases your chances of weight loss on a long-term basis, as well as learning to value your food.

Learn about your hunger scale. Identify your emotional and physical state before and after eating. Notice any patterns and habits that contribute to your hunger scale. Never allow yourself to get to a starving painful point or eating until you are stuff.

Remaining in the middle of the scale will allow you to eat healthy portions and enjoy the process; therefore, you will not be in pain.

Day 11:

Day 11 explores the relationship between the food industry and weight loss. Food advertising increases psychological hunger in adults. Many adults who have struggled with weight loss began noticing fast food advertising when they were young. You were programmed to respond physically to commercials of fast food while watching television. The relationship between television and fast food is carefully negotiated and cultivated for decades, and learning how to combat and prevent falling for the trap is essential to healthy living.

Researchers have discovered that adults exposed to unhealthy food advertisements ate more than those watching nutritious food messages. This study reveals a link to how unhealthy food advertisements increase snacking while watching television in adults. Eating mindlessly is a common habit among adults who suffer from excessive weight.

A healthy habit recommendation to prevent mindless eating is to avoid watching television while eating. The habit of eating in front of the television is engrained with adults and is a habit that may need negotiating to ease off of slowly. You should start by not eating at least half of your meal in front of the television.

If you choose to eat while watching television, you must have specific portions to prevent overeating. This means no giant bags of chips or rolls of crackers or cookies. Have a set amount in a small bowl that requires you to get up when you finish your portion. This will train you not to eat mindlessly and assess your level of hunger.

After you have lessened your portions while snacking, you can then incorporate more healthy snacks. Some healthy snacks to eat if you choose to eat while watching television include vegetables, fruits, nuts, and popcorn in portion-controlled sizes.

Along with food advertisements that can harm your healthy changes and progress, is the overall food industry. The food industry as a whole is filled with harmful ingredients that increase hunger and cravings. If you do not feel secure in grocery shopping, you should never go when you are hungry because your hunger increases impulsive buying of unhealthy foods.

Another suggestion to avoid an impulse to buy in a grocery store is for you to only shop off your pre-planned shopping list. This list coincides with your organized meal plan for the week. Having an organized food plan allows for a rigid shopping structure where you will not feel the pressure to buy junk food.

To avoid impulse buying, having an awareness of the tricks supermarket advertising use on their consumers will decrease your impulsive buying. When shopping, junk food is advertised twice as often as healthy foods. This means that chocolate, chips, ice cream, high-sugar breakfast cereals are discounted to encourage purchasing.

Along with discounts on junk food, there are also increased discounts on sugar-sweetened beverages. These drinks include soft drinks, sports and energy drinks. These drinks are discounted double as often as milk and water. Awareness while shopping will lessen your likelihood of purchasing due to guilt or pressure.

The psychology behind why supermarkets increase discounts on junk food is due to the impulsive nature of junk food. Junk food, by its concept, is to service your cravings, whether these cravings are for sweet, savory, salty, or spice food. The major discounts persuade customers to buy because of the appearance of saving money. In reality, your health costs increase due to the harmful ingredients these foods contribute toward your health.

Along with supermarket advertising, there is television advertising, which also influences consumers. Fast food ads promote their ultra-processed foods that influence customers to eat even when they are not hungry. The bright colors and appealing nature of the food entice viewers to eat the food regardless of their lack of physical hunger. The suggestion of the food based on its appearance drives many consumers into purchasing fast food.

Along with advertising and influencing your decisions regarding snacking and junk food eating, there is also a deep emotional bond between fast food and consumers. Many adults with weight issues grew up with fast food as a fun experience that was shared with their family as children and continued through adulthood. Positive memories are linked with this brand of food, but your health deteriorates because of the negative effect the ingredients have on your health.

You need to break apart your emotional attachments toward this version of the food. It is not an authentic relationship and only continues to support your emotional eating habits. You do not owe these large corporations loyalty when they damage your health. This is a one-way relationship that needs to be cut out and extinguished from your life.

Along with junk food advertising indoctrinating you at an early age for brand loyalty, you are also exposed to weight loss advertising. Differentiating between weight loss programs and products helps to find what works best for you. This includes researching all of the different apps, fitness trackers, budget gyms, weight loss clinics, weight loss supplements, and meal planning services.

Along with rampant fast food advertising, the weight loss industry is also a billion-dollar industry that is one of the biggest and most profitable. Confusion and uncertainty are emotions that this business preys upon to convince you to buy their products. Before buying any weight loss product, you must consult with a licensed professional. This can include your primary care doctor, dietician, or personal trainer before buying any medicine that will "guarantee" weight loss.

Weight loss guru's for national companies are salespeople who have the overall goal of selling you a particular brand or product, regardless of whether it actually affects your health in a positive way or not. You need to receive accurate advice through knowledgeable and reputable sources. This information will limit the possibility of you being taken advantage of.

Your money has value, and your spending should reflect and work with your weight loss plan and goals. Your goals should include regular exercise and nutritious eating. Starting these two habits is critical, and talking to your doctor makes it possible to take a productive step in addressing your health.

In Summation:

Awareness of advertisements and psychological programming of grocery stores is essential in combating possible troubling food habits and situations. In order to prevent unwanted weight gain and setbacks, it is recommended that you do not eat in front of a television.

Eating in front of a television increases the likelihood of overeating due to the distractions of technology. While eating, you need to focus on the food in front of you and learn to eat regularly and slowly. By starting this new habit, you must remain consistent throughout your weight loss process.

Also, eating in front of the television causes you mindlessly eat and remain unable to tell when you are full or satisfied.

Food commercials promote unhealthy food options that increase psychological hunger. Understanding these traps and reading them more clearly allows you to stay on track for your health.

Having a concrete grocery list and meal plan also helps in preventing unnecessary food purchases and impulse buys.

Understanding the psychology behind the placement of certain items at the grocery improves your ability to resist impulsive buying.

Day 12:

Day 12 focuses on the various issues with digestion when eating. This includes feeling full from eating too much or too little. Listening and observing how your body reacts to its food is a key skill in this four-week weight loss plan.

In your second week, you were taught to understand the difference between psychological hunger and physical hunger. Now, you will place your attention on how you would know if your full feelings are healthy or not. Many adults who have dealt with disordered eating habits and patterns no longer understand the difference between a healthy fullness and unhealthy fullness. Adults with an excessive weight typically overindulge because they are not well informed on listening to their bodies.

In essence, fullness is the feeling of being satisfied. Your stomach tells your brain that you are full. This feeling causes you to stop eating and cease thinking about food for several hours. When you are distracted, you will lack the ability to recognize your body's cues for its fullness.

Some helpful tools in listening to natural body cues of fullness include eating slowly with minimal technological distractions. Cell phones and television bring endless amounts of distractions from concentrating on your food. Once you have limited your distractions, you can then focus intentionally on the food in front of you.

With limited distractions, you are able to eat intentionally and slowly. It takes roughly twenty minutes to recognize whether or not you are full after eating, but if you are eating too much food too quickly, you will overeat.

A sign for you to know that you are full while you're eating is when you need to breathe before you take your next bite. This means that you're full. If you don't stop, you're going to overeat. When you need to relax for a while before you go on eating, it's your body's way of showing you're full.

A sign for you to be aware that you are overeating too often is when you have a full feeling where you can't move and breathe. This may be similar to eating after a Thanksgiving dinner. Eating larger portions and heavier foods leads to overeating. This experience is one you need to work on avoiding.

To avoid the chance of overeating during your meals, you can lighten your meals by having a protein-based meal instead of a high starch or fat food-focused meal. A protein-based meal is recommended because they are lower in calories and higher in fiber, which will make you feel fuller faster. Other foods to include with your meals are foods with high fiber, which include grains, legumes, and vegetables.

On the opposite end of the spectrum, you should also avoid feeling full after eating very little. This is the opposite of overeating, and it occurs when you continuously feel full sooner than normal or after eating less than usual. Some side effects may include nausea, vomiting, bloating, or weight loss. These signs can indicate digestion trouble and should be carefully monitored.

Another sign to monitor why listening to your physical body cues is whether or not you have regular upset stomachs. This includes stomach pains or feelings of fullness soon after you have started eating. Symptoms of indigestion include having early fullness during a meal where you have not eaten much of your meal, but you already feel full and cannot finish your meal. Other signs are uncomfortable fullness after a meal that lasts longer than it should. Either experience indicates trouble with your health and should be carefully monitored. If there is no improvement with an antacid, you should see a doctor. There may be other complications within your stomach lining.

Other signs of digestion problems are discomfort in your upper abdomen that can increase from mild to severe pain. You may also encounter nausea to the point you want to vomit, and feeling bloated. The cause of indigestion is varied, but it's usually connected with eating too quickly, eating fatty, greasy, or spicy foods, having too much caffeine, alcohol, or carbonated beverages in your system.

To treat digestion problems, you will need to adapt to a different, healthier lifestyle. With your weight loss plan, you have started incorporating healthier eating habits and regular exercise. You have included different foods into your diet that will challenge your stomach and digestive system. With your new lifestyle, you should continue avoiding foods that are fatty, highly seasoned, and difficult to digest.

Along with carefully monitoring your food choices, you would need to eat slowly, mindfully, and intuitively. Smaller meals also allow your stomach to digest the food at a slower rate. You will also decrease your chance of overeating when your portions are smaller and more contained.

Along with changing your eating habits, limiting your drinking of caffeine and alcohol will make your stomach more comfortable and decrease the odds of a negative reaction as your digestive system adapts to the new habits.

As you incorporate new foods into your diet and remove possible damaging foods, you need to continue a regular exercise routine. Exercising helps maintain your digestive system and decreases any uncomfortable sensations that occur with eating new and different foods.

Overall, the main takeaway is listening to your natural body cues that are influenced by your lifestyle. Your behavior plays a significant role in how your body responds. This means that you need to improve your own awareness by knowing your limits and weaknesses. The only way you will learn your boundaries is taking things slowly. Introduce new foods to your diet carefully and monitor the reaction your digestion system has to its inclusion.

If you often overeat, you need to dedicate time each week to tune into your thoughts and needs of your body and how they are connected with food. Overeating regularly defeats the purpose of healthy eating because of the stress and pressure your stomach is enduring to rebalance your body towards a more comfortable state.

To develop a better relationship with food, you need to know where you struggle to prevent digestion issues.

In Summation:

Overeating is a habit common with many adults with disordered eating patterns. These habits are well established and require strong amounts of discipline and attention. First, limit your distractions when eating. When you do eat, you need to eat slowly and regularly.

After your eating habits have improved, you must not rush your dining experience. It takes a minimum of twenty minutes for your stomach and brain to communicate a feeling of fullness. Your feeling of fullness will leave a satisfying sensation. This will stop your feelings of hunger, but only when you take the necessary amount of time between bites.

Digestion can include many different eating experiences. Common negative experiences include stomach heaviness and indigestion. If this is a common experience, then your food choices and behaviors may be the culprit. Modifying your lifestyle is critical as you listen to your body and its response to certain foods.

To help prevent digestion issues, you need to learn how to make wise food choices. This means eating a balanced diet that is slower to digest and makes you feel fuller longer.

Day 13:

Day 13 focuses on your exercise routine. By the end of week two, you should have started a routine that is comfortable and slightly challenging. Your routine should include some form of cardio and weight training. Exercising complements your healthy eating habits and increases your weight loss, as well as improving your physical and mental health. Exercise is also helpful for weight loss and maintaining weight loss.

Exercise increases your metabolism and the number of calories you burn in a day. Exercise can also help you maintain and increase lean body mass, which also helps increase the number of calories you burn each day.

Combining exercise with a healthy diet is the most effective way to lose weight rather than depending on calorie restrictions alone. Exercise also prevents or reverses the effects of certain diseases. It also lowers blood pressure, cholesterol, and this limits the likelihood of a heart attack.

Many exercises help you lose weight. Some optimal choices for burning calories include walking, jogging, running, cycling, swimming, weight training, interval training, yoga, and Pilates. Choosing an exercise routine in which you enjoy doing, increases the likelihood of long term success with promising results.

Your exercise program needs to use an aerobic form of exercise. Aerobic exercises increase your heart rate and promote blood flow. Aerobic exercises include walking, jogging, cycling, swimming, and dancing. You can also diversify your exercise routine by working out on a fitness machine such as a treadmill, elliptical, or stair stepper.

Walking is the recommended starting point for exercise. This is recommended for beginning your weight loss program because you are able to pick speed, incline, and resistance when on a treadmill. Walking allows you not to become overwhelmed due to its low impact that does not stress your joints.

Walking can also be used in many aspects of your daily life. You can take a walk during a lunch break at work, by taking the stairs at work or taking your pet on extra walks throughout the day. Any way to have more exercise throughout your day promotes a healthier lifestyle and improves mental health as well.

A helpful starting point is walking for thirty minutes 3-4 times a week. This can increase as you become more comfortable in your fitness. You can increase to 5-6 times a week after two weeks of consistent walking, then eventually start walking every day. The goal is to have a daily exercise where it becomes part of your daily routine and is no longer designated as your exercise time.

Another exercise routine to add as you become more comfortable with increased activity is weight training. Weight training builds strength and promotes muscle growth, which increases the number of calories your body burns. Your body will burn more calories as you shed more fat. To maximize fat loss, you need to also minimize muscle loss. By minimizing muscle loss, your health can be maintained longer because your strength has increased.

Alongside cardio and weight training, yoga is also recommended to relieve stress and lose weight.

Yoga is not as intense as other types of exercise, but you can practice mindfulness. Mindfulness, as previously discussed, helps you resist unhealthy foods, control overeating, and better understand your body's hunger signals. Yoga classes are offered at many gyms, or you can practice in your home.

The total amount of exercise you do during a day is more important than whether or not you do it in a single session. Small changes to your daily routine make a big difference.

Healthy lifestyle habits to increase your activity include walking or riding your bike to work or while running errands. You can also increase your activity by taking the stairs instead of the elevator and parking farther away from your destinations and walking the remaining distance.

All of these activities aid in your weight loss journey because weight loss has to include both healthy eating habits and exercise. Exercise and eating healthy are integral aspects of your new health journey. By joining new exercise classes, you can expand your social circle to include more active adults on a similar journey as yourself.

This expansion of your social life promotes sustainable weight loss due to increased accountability from others. Sharing your goals with others with similar goals helps to promote a healthy community in your life that is not as lonely.

Exercise helps contribute to an increased sense of confidence and well-being. This connection lowers your rate of anxiety and depression. Weight loss and decreased rates of depression are connected because exercise increases serotonin, which makes you feel better. When you feel better, your mind relaxes and reduces stress and anxiety.

An important distinction is that exercise lacks all importance when your nutrition is not balanced.

In Summation:

A consistent exercise routine enhances your already cultivated food routine. Exercise can take many forms. A great start to cardio is walking 3-4 times a week for thirty minutes. You can increase your resistance as you grow more comfortable with walking.

Alongside walking, there are other exercises you can add to your plan. These exercises with low impact on your joints include yoga, swimming, and weight training.

There are many classes you can take to foster your new exercises, and choosing an enjoyable class helps you to continue after your four weeks of health-focused dedication.

Exercise and healthy eating work alongside your weight loss goals. You need to combine both aspects of your health. Exercise and diet need to work with one another.

Day 14:

Congratulations on reaching the midway point in your weight loss plan. Day 14 focuses on addressing all your hard work and determination in changing your health. Your constant attention and focus on your eating habits and exercises test your commitment. The hard work required to address your history with food is not a simple task. This plan forces you to confront all aspects of your psychological history with food.

With all of your positive transformative changes, you also experience moments of personal doubt. You may feel ashamed at not making a goal weight or splurging on a small dessert. All of these will not stop your weight loss from continuing. These are part of the process as you learn how to navigate stress.

Many adults struggle with negative uncertain thoughts while on their weight loss journey. Obsessing over a specific goal weight creates unnecessary anxiety and difficulty in maintaining your newly cultivated habits. Practicing patience and forgiveness with yourself as you work on changing your life on the inside and outside should be acknowledged and appreciated. It is okay to make mistakes because they are part of your human experience.

Day 14 highlights the dark thoughts that can come from dieting. The obsessive thinking and rigidity that often accompanies documenting your daily food. The habits are important, but having a perfectionist outlook is damaging to your health and its progress. Learning to accept mistakes, flaws, and loosening the tight rope on your eating habit is essential once you've got the proper habits down.

If your habits are still not secure, you should still be strict with yourself.

Obsessing over your weight can take many forms, but an unhealthy obsession with your diet can develop into an eating disorder. A recognized eating disorder is having Orthorexia or extreme healthy eating.

Orthorexia is an eating disorder where you determine the quality of your food, have rigid eating patterns, have severe emotional turmoil when your rules are broken, cut off whole groups of food, and are constantly worried about getting sick.

Having a fixation over the quality of food you have is the core of an obsessive eating disorder. You will often become focused on the quality and purity of your food. You limit your food options to only organic, fresh, whole, and raw or vegan. Although these are positive qualities in food, the portion size is more important in weight loss than the label.

Another sign of obsessive eating pattern is inflexibility. This happens when you are rigid and immovable with your eating routine. You avoid anything that can be interpreted as unhealthy and sometimes refrain from eating anything altogether.

Obsessive eating patterns also occur when you have an extreme reaction to breaking a food rule. By breaking a rule, you have extreme anxiety, distress, shame, and guilt towards yourself. This is a sign that you have developed an unhealthful eating pattern that needs to be addressed.

Furthermore, eliminating entire food groups indicates a form of obsessive thinking. You will also experience a need to self-isolate from social situations because you are afraid of exposing yourself to forbidden foods. This avoidance technique is unhealthy and can lead to a depressive episode and other intense negative thoughts and actions.

Along with food obsession is starvation. Starving your body from food causes you to actually gain or retain weight because you are holding on to fat. Fat is essential to your body that energizes your body, and if you are not giving your body enough nutrients, your body will begin to shut down.

Obsession and starving yourself of food is a dangerous road you should not venture into. Most of this anxiety-driven thinking originates from having low self-esteem. If you have obsessive thoughts of starving yourself, you should seek out counseling to share your thoughts and frustrations. Shifting your view from the value that comes solely from a number to appreciate the overall lifestyle is a legitimate change of perspective.

Low self-esteem increases with mental insults that lead to long states of depression. This increases your stress responses that store fat. Building a strong community and environment that includes positive thinking and expressions will help you in creating a better relationship with your body instead of constant criticism and put-downs.

A recommended approach for lessening obsessive thoughts surrounding weight loss includes incorporating meaningful goals. A meaningful goal takes into account less specific end goal results like a weight on the scale and offers a more holistic approach.

Changing your approach to how you view diet and exercise to lower anxiety and obsessive thoughts include: having more energy to accomplish more each day, getting a better quality of sleep each night, increased concentration, increased body awareness, decreased stress, and increases your bodily strength.

Incorporating changes in how you view your mind and body will promote a healthier mindset on your weight loss journey. Losing weight is both a mental and physical journey where both must work together for optimal success. These small changes in your approach to diet and exercise will help lessen any obsessive tendencies.

Another way to lessen your obsessive thoughts regarding weight loss is by adding more functional weight loss goals. These goals offer a positive approach to diet and exercise through the changes to your mind and body.

Some small, but obvious non-scale related victories you can see or feel are increased positive moods, which can lessen depressive episodes. Increased creativity is a common side effect of exercise, also having more energy due to increase your energy. Your stress levels will also decrease readily, especially when you are using yoga exercises that calm the mind and make the body to relax.

With all of these positive changes to your body, your anxiety will naturally go down, which will also lower your blood pressure due to increased circulation and blood flow. Other goals may take more time to appear, but these are obvious signs and symptoms of increased regular exercise that reduces many negative side effects of adult obesity.

To help lessen negative thoughts and behaviors with your weight loss, you must begin by improving your self-esteem towards your body image. Options for improving body image include positive affirmations and meeting with a certified eating disorder therapist.

You will be able to vocalize your confidence issues and perfectionism habits and thoughts.

Allowing time to improve your mental and physical conditions is the only treatment that can positively change your life in the long term.

In Summation:

You are midway through your weight loss plan.

Healthy eating is not a skill that is learned overnight. You must exercise patience with yourself to learn and adapt to the changes in a healthy manner.

Starving and obsessing over every food decision is not helpful and will actually cease your weight loss progress. You must be gentle and kind to yourself. Allow imperfections on your journey.

The human experience functions best as a journey of learning how to incorporate food into your life. Fearing food will limit your chances of success.

Talking with a licensed eating disorder therapist is strongly encouraged as you navigate your thoughts and emotions towards food.

Week 3:

Day 15:

Congratulations on beginning the third week of your weight loss program. Your determination to improve and cultivate a balanced life is acknowledged and appreciated. Your hard work allows your mind and body to change. There are a lot of positive changes while you're pursuing your goals, but there's also a hard time staying motivated for your new lifestyle.

Your dedication toward your health and wellness will often be a struggle. Learning to ride a bike is a perfect metaphor that resembles a journey of weight loss. You will fall many times before you get the hang of it, and even after you have learned it, there will be struggles, but you still get back on. This mentality is the same approach you should have to weight loss. Learning to overcome setbacks and not feeling defeated or disappointed is essential in maintaining your weight loss journey.

This weight loss plan is not only about eating habits. If you are concentrating only on how much, how often, or on what you are eating, you will self-combust. Weight loss cannot survive on alternating your eating habits alone. To have a successful weight loss, you need to integrate changes in your eating, exercising, and mental health. Many adults who fall off the wagon in their weight loss program forget to include every aspect of health with their lifestyle.

Pursuing a well-balanced and healthy life will have its discouraging moments. From time to time, you will lose sight of your goals and fall off. This experience is completely natural and common. There is no shame in admitting that you will struggle. The important part is learning how to recover when you relapse back into old habits.

Research shows that many overweight adults are able to keep off their weight long term by problem-solving.

Problem-solving includes having the insight to realize when you are slipping off course or have already slipped and fallen off course. Once you realize that you have fallen off course, you need to reach out to your support system. This system can include a community of friends, family, or professionals that can help you gain new perspective and control within your life.

An example of falling off course is eating dessert every night after dinner even when you are not hungry. You are stressed at work and need a distraction that makes you feel good. Eat cake once a week or once a month does not ruin your health, but creating the habit of rewarding your stress with comfort food is dangerous behavior.

Many adults find it difficult to maintain their health changes and habits due to a variety of factors. Ways to combat and survive personal, professional, or familial devastation is reminding yourself of your reason for starting this weight loss program.

Back in week 1, the first day of this program, you were asked to define your reason. Remind yourself why you are still on this journey. The sky is the limit for your reason, ranging from simple vanity to improving your mental or physical health. Whatever your reason is, now is the time to remind yourself of why you are choosing to get back on track.

Your mind is strong and resilient. Overweight adults have struggled with numerous diets throughout their life. Dieting experiences are filled with temporary success and long periods of regret, shame, and inevitable regain. Learning how to use your mind as a weapon in focusing on your goals is important to achieve them.

When you are tempted to abandon your healthy eating and exercise plan, you need to remind yourself why your health is worth all of your daily pain, sacrifice, and struggle. Losing and gaining excessive amounts of weight promotes stress on your cardiovascular system, which increases your chance of heart disease.

Along with cultivating a healthy mind and strengthening your will power, you need to remind yourself of your new healthy habits. Your negative behaviors lead to weight gain, which prevents you from reaching your goal. These behaviors that have made you lose track of your goals need to change. Remember that you are in charge of your environment; you decide what food you buy and eat. Having healthy foods in your home promotes your weight loss goals.

Having healthy food options also limits the likelihood of overeating on greasy and fattening foods. Stocking up on healthy snacks and meals will lessen the struggle in unhealthy eating. Some healthy snack options are carrots, peanuts, apples, and bananas. These are healthier options that will not increase your waistline.

Healthy food options are only possible with reliable and consistent meal planning. Planning healthy meals allows time to divide everything into accurate portion sizes. Take one day a week to cook and divide your meals into proper portions; many people choose Sundays.

If cooking is not a personal strength of yours, you can also make small purchases that are already divided into small portions. Some examples are single-served almond pouches or yogurt cups that make eating on the go easy.

Cooking all your meals on the same day saves time and energy. Cooking all at once can be as simple and easy as using a crockpot for cooking shredded chicken during the day as a healthy protein and using a steamer to heat vegetables.

Along with recommitting yourself to a healthy diet, you will need to nourish your body. You cannot deprive yourself of essential nutrients to lose weight. Undereating increases your chances of binging and overeating. To eliminate starving tendencies, you can include planned snacks in your routine to allow yourself a healthy food schedule. By giving yourself time to eat, you can monitor your portions and prevent under and overeating.

In addition to loosening your reigns with obsessive eating strategies, you may have started dining more frequently than your routine cements. You may have eaten foods that are not on your pre-approved eating plan. Dining out can promote many instances of overeating. The foods are rich with supersized portions that make sticking to your goals difficult. The challenge you will have to remind yourself is portion control.

Ways to promote proper portion control is bringing Tupperware to the restaurants and taking away the excess food before you even start eating. Furthermore, if you are not too hungry, you can think about ordering an appetizer instead of a full entrée. These are simple tricks to dining out to prevent you from stressing over the many possible temptations.

Along with reexamining your food habits, you need to also reevaluate your food tracking. Look into whether or not you are too flexible or rigid in your food choices. This may indicate why you are struggling during your third week because you have developed a perfectionist mentality towards weight loss.

You need to reward yourself when you make consistent healthy decisions. Some examples include having one brownie every Friday in celebration of all your hard work. Whatever a treat is to you should be rewarded to commend your healthy behavior. This reward system also prevents unwanted cravings, which are uncomfortable during your weight loss.

Along with physical rewards, you also need to reward yourself mentally. Mental rewards begin with forgiving yourself from negative choices and practicing patience as you learn from your mistakes.

Indulging yourself during a celebration or holiday does not require a later shaming episode where you belittle yourself. Learning how to curb your judgmental tendencies is a difficult and challenging task. Do not expect to lose the weight immediately; it took time to put the weight on, so it will take time to come off as well.

Other ways to put yourself back on track is reevaluating how often you count your calories. Decreasing the number of calories you consume daily is important when losing weight, but you may become malnourished when you are depriving your body of essential nutrients. Your body will not be able to work properly if you do not have enough nutrients from the calories you consume.

Adults with weight issues often judge others and themselves critically. They judge their past and present actions and ridiculous choices when they see them as mistakes. Having a judgmental outlook on every action naturally affects your relationship with yourself and others. Learn to incorporate positive influences in your life.

If you do not have a positive group of people that can support your lifestyle changes, you will need to shift your priorities. You cannot achieve your health goals by yourself because your entire motivation cannot come solely from you alone. If you have started this journey alone and you are currently alone, then you need to expand and include others into your private circle.

Start small and slowly branch out. Expanding your network may include joining an exercise class or online chat forum. Anywhere that will bring positive reinforcement is better.

Allow yourself time to change and grow. You will not change your entire outlook overnight, but reading and listening to body positive and health experts will provide a great foundation in increasing your self-confidence and change your attitude towards others and yourself.

In Summation:

The beginning of the third week of your weight loss routine focuses on reevaluating your goals and priorities. Many adults lose their momentum after 7 to 14 days after starting a diet or exercise routine. Refocusing and aligning your mind and body with your previously stated goals is a great way to get back on track.

Examine your food log and notice any emotional patterns. Examine your environment and decide whether or not it is hospitable for healthy food. Decide if or not you are damaging your health with unhealthy foods to quell your cravings.

Remember to be gentle and patient with yourself as you work hard in correcting your mistakes and learning from your experiences. Weight loss is successful when your habits go along with your lifestyle choices. Do not focus solely on exercising or dieting because your entire well-being must be included with your weight loss journey.

Day 16:

Day 16 tackles the confounding feelings of shame and guilt during weight loss. It is good to think about what you eat, how much, and when you eat. Feelings of blame, guilt, and shame after eating something indulgent create problems with weight loss. These feelings allow your mind to place barriers in your weight management. Training your mind to notice indulgences will help you with weight loss by learning how to avoid and change your behavior.

Blame is the feeling of finding fault with yourself or holding yourself responsible when you think that what you've done is "bad." Common feelings that follow blaming yourself are anger, frustration, and anxiety. These feelings lead to mental health struggles. Reframing your mind is essential in overcoming these negative impulses. Instead of blaming yourself for any food indiscretion, you need to understand why you behaved the way you did. Once you understand what led to your food choice, the more capable you will be in preventing the same reaction from happening.

Indulging in delicious food is a vital part of life. To learn how to enjoy food, you need to start celebrating your choices and learning from them instead of shaming your actions. It is not sustainable to never let yourself have something sweet or savory. Eating something that tastes good helps feed your soul and keep you motivated on your weight loss journey.

Guilt should not occur when you have a treat, but you need to monitor the amount. Overindulging can lead to feeling bloated and sluggish because your digestion system is not used to the food you are eating.

Guilt can either be a great way to motivate your goals, but often leads to out of control feelings. Guilt increases your negative outlook on your body image. By feeling guilty, you feel unhealthier, which will make you want to eat more.

The feelings of guilt and shame are extremely dangerous to binge eaters who are in recovery because excessive guilt and shame lead to unhealthy expectations of yourself. Guilt is used in a healthy way to increase empathy with others and yourself. However, eating disorderly causes overeating or under eating to correct behavior.

Instead of inducing a guilt reaction when you're eating outside of your food plan, practice compassion. Compassion includes treating yourself the way you would want to treat others in your situation. You are choosing kindness with yourself instead of anger and frustration. Mistakes are expected and allowed in your human life. Practice allowing moments of imperfection and do not beat yourself up.

To improve your eating behavior after you have had many slip-ups with your eating plan, you should be able to reflect on your actions. Reflecting on your actions helps you understand why they happened in the first place. Noticing your actions and learning from them allows you to let the guilt move along and not linger. Lingering guilt serves no purpose in promoting healthy eating. Guilt is often used negatively and leads to an overeating episode.

An example of associating guilt with food choices occurs when you think you are eating something "bad." Eating away from your diet plan leads you to feel and think the thoughts of disappointment and shame in your choices. You feel "weak" or "pathetic" because you cannot stop yourself from indulging in cookies or brownies. Due to the fact that you are so depleted mentally, you then tell yourself that you should eat more because you are already "weak," so why bother stopping. Eventually, you eat the entire chocolate cake or plate of brownies. This is a classic example of overeating due to guilt and shame.

To combat this unhealthy cycle of mental abuse, you need to pause yourself when you feel angry or disappointed with your food choices. You need to quit yelling at yourself and acknowledge your mistake. Mistakes happen, and you need to learn to let them go. Guilt fuels disordered eating patterns. Learning from your mistakes allows you to reclaim your sense of control with eating

In order to prevent yourself from losing control over your eating choices, it is advisable for you to plan when and how often you will indulge in your cravings. This can be a planned day every week where you allow yourself to eat one cookie, piece of cake, or brownie. By choosing when, how much, and where, brings a sense of control back into your environment. Allowing a celebration of your healthy choices by a small indulgence gives the incentive to motivate you forward on your health journey.

Learning when you are getting carried away with negative feelings takes time and practice in navigating. Gaining proper insight means taking time and energy to listen to your thoughts and think about how you can respond. Committing to your goals is essential, but allowing rewards and gifts along the way makes your journey more survivable.

If you are still struggling with positively reinforcing yourself back into healthy habits, then you should try finding an encouraging resource to find motivation. Children need encouragement when they fail at something, and so do adults. Weight loss is one of the most challenging attempts at change. Change does not happen overnight, but with this weight loss plan, you are learning the necessary tools and finding resources that lessen the workload.

Ways to incorporate a more positive outlook and a relationship with food begin with compassion. This begins by acknowledging your mistakes and reaffirming your commitment to your goals. This works by stating that you're going to change your actions tomorrow and that it's okay for you to eat two brownies today.

Another positive change that you can incorporate in the writing of your values. These values are what you want to live by, so when you feel guilty about your food choices, you can remember your written values.

Another food takeaway is realizing that you'll never remember exactly what you've eaten at your meal in the last five years, five months, five weeks, or five days, but the lasting impression is the experience. The memories you hold of the people you share with them are more valuable than the food you eat.

These are some healthy tools to incorporate to learn how to stop judging your food choices. You will never make perfect decisions all the time, which is okay.

In Summation:

Food guilt, blame, and shame are common with overweight adults. Your weight is personal and private, but unfortunately, everyone feels that their opinion on your body and health is accepted and appreciated.

The only opinion that matters is yours, but when you are attacking your own thoughts and actions towards food, then you are belittling all your hard work and progress.

Shaming your actions only leads to more episodes of disordered eating. You need to learn empathy and compassion for your food choices.

Talking with a counselor is recommended to improve the image you have of yourself. Your weight loss journey can be lonely, and having a support system helps lift the pressure.

Day 17:

Day 17 focuses on distinguishing between traps and triggers that affect your emotional and physical health with weight management. Triggers are certain foods, situations, and feelings that prompt you to overeat and gain weight or prevent current or future weight loss. You have different triggers when you are on a diet. For some people, boredom is a trigger, while for others, it's stress. For some, it's a social event, and for others, it is when they are alone. Your triggers are barriers to a successful weight loss.

Overweight adults struggle with identifying and controlling their trigger foods, situations, and feelings. By not controlling your reaction in certain situations, you overeat. You need to change the mentality of "I am out of control," into "No, I am in control."

A triggered response occurs slowly. Something catches your attention that persuades you to eat a cookie that you have not eaten for three weeks since starting your weight loss plan. You are feeling stressed from a long day at work, and the smell of baked goods makes you salivate. You feel deprived of cookies from dieting for three weeks and want to have a treat.

You begin eating one cookie, which leads to three, and then you go on to eat an entire sleeve of Samoa Girl Scout cookies. You have lost control due to your compromised emotional state. When you are committed to a certain diet plan, you are in control and choosing to move away from that plan puts you in an out of control state. Certain foods, eaten at certain places when you have specific feelings, control your actions.

To learn how to control your behavior, you need to first have to become aware of the influence certain emotional states have on your actions. Awareness is essential in preventing other overeating episodes.

First, you need to identify the foods, feelings, and situations that cause you to overeat. You can find this out by reading your food journal or reflecting on your emotional states throughout the day or week. You will notice a pattern.

After reading your journal, you can then decide how you will respond to this information. You have to make a mental choice before you can react intentionally. You can control your triggers by stopping your response. Conditioned eating habit is only able to stop when you actively stop eating. For many adults with weight loss issues, this needs to be a permanent decision.

Having absolute control means deciding where, when, and what you're going to eating. Choosing how you respond to this is controlling your trigger. This doesn't mean you can never have a Girl Scout cookie again; it's just not when you're tired or stressed out of work that you can engage in over-indulging in cookies. This is a specific behavior that you no longer accept.

The only way for your response to become permanent is through practice. With your awareness and understanding, you can prepare your responses before they occur. You will decide in advance that your next stressful day at work will not end with you eating an entire sleeve of Girl Scout cookies. You will consciously decide that this is not your reaction. Instead, you'll eat carrots, or go for a walk, or listen to music.

Along with understanding your triggers on personal experience, there are occasions where food is the central activity. Many holidays and celebrations revolve around food, which can be emotionally difficult for many adults learning to manage their eating habits.

You are conditioned to expect food for comfort, not nourishment. Learning how to navigate your emotions in a healthy way can improve your likelihood of sticking to your health plan. Emotional eating allows an escape from dealing with your feelings directly. Your feelings are the biggest indicator of your current emotional state, and it allows you to learn from your actions and experiences.

You are able to rewire your brain in four weeks through cultivating healthy habits. A habit takes at minimum one month to form. Your new habits of healthy snacking and daily exercise provide a great starting point for healthy living.

Along with your daily habits, you also need to limit your exposure to processed food. Processed food is often connected with emotions. Overindulging when your emotions are compromised is common with large portions of processed food.

Alongside rewiring your brain, you also need to stop restricting your body from nutrients. Emotional eating is usually connected to restriction. Restrictive eating includes waiting too long to eat and not eating the necessary foods. This leads to overeating and emotional eating because you are hungry. Sticking to a regular eating plan that allows time to assess how you feel before, during, and after eating. On the hunger scale, you should reside at a 5 or 6 of satisfaction and fullness.

You are emotionally compromised when you are stressed, skipping meals, not exercising, and not sleeping well. Having a strong foundation of these core values and habits is vital for prolonged weight loss success.

Regular exercise and having a balanced nutritious diet is easy in theory but can be difficult to maintain due to many setbacks in life that are out of your control. It is important to have a solid foundation that promotes a positive and healthy mental state and outlook.

If you need further help and assistance with navigating your weight loss, then you should reach out to a professional dietician or counselor.

In Summation:

Emotional triggers lead to behaviors that damage your progress with weight loss. Stress becomes too much to handle, and you revert to a comfortable habit you have used in the past.

This chain reaction is a conditioned and learned response that shows that you are capable of stopping with the right amount of awareness and attention.

You are able to choose and change how you react by consciously deciding beforehand. This can appear impossible, but learning the right coping skills allows the chain reaction to stop.

Eating emotionally is a habit that is socially cultivated and accepted. Many social functions are surrounded and themed around food. Having this awareness allows you to plan your food choices and prevent stress from occurring. You know yourself better than anyone, and you need to reflect upon your actions. Taking time better prepares you for success and tackling your emotional triggers for the future.

Day 18:

Day 18 focuses on your social life as you continue on your weight loss journey. Increasing your social interactions can be a daunting task when you have battled with your weight for years and have low self-esteem.

As you tackle your weight in a direct way through this weight loss program, you increase your social interactions. Increasing your social interactions increases your confidence, which motivates you to continue losing weight. Social interactions can often be challenging and stressful, but with increasing your activity individually, you can slowly increase your interactions socially.

Your new healthy lifestyle is only possible with your own dedication, which is increased through your interaction with others. Establish your eating habits and maintain a healthy weight. This concept is difficult when you do it alone. Increasing your social circle is essential to improve your health patterns.

You can embark on increasing your social interactions by discussing your weight struggles and goals with friends and family. You can also discuss your goals and thoughts only if you feel safe and supported by your chosen group. By including others in your program, you develop a strong support system. You can open up and speak freely about how much reaching your goal weight means to you. You can share what you expect to gain and lose throughout this process.

On the other side, you need to be aware that many diet saboteurs hide in plain sight. These problematic people are often your family, friends, and colleagues. They can either be directly negative and pessimistic about your weight loss goals or passive-aggressive because of their own failed attempts at weight loss. It is important to monitor how often they discourage your weight loss and understand their comments are due to their envy.

Be mindful of who you choose to let inside your special circle of confidantes. Not everyone is supportive in the right way.

An important aspect of weight loss is finding a person or group that you can share on your journey. This can include joining an exercise class or finding an exercise buddy. These confidants are able to offer you supportive advice and companionship. You need support because the mental and physical stress that comes from lifestyle changes is natural and challenging.

You will experience withdrawal symptoms and low-will power due to the desire to engage with unhealthy and sabotaging food. It takes a minimum of one month for habits to form and become cemented. You will be tempted many times throughout your first month and every month after that with lessening degrees to cheat on your health plan.

The difficult and challenging aspect of weight loss is that it does not instantly make you happier or improve your body image. Weight loss challenges your relationships with friends and loved ones. You may experience immediate positive mental and emotional changes with little impact on your relationship. More importantly, your loved ones will need time to support your changes as they are perceived negatively. Your circle of friends and family are adjusting to your health changes. This period of transition and change offers new opportunities for growth and reflection for your friends and family.

Your body image is the most common struggle that overweight adults encounter regularly. Self-image is connected to phantom fat syndrome. This syndrome is common in people who have had major weight loss. You may have had major weight loss and struggle currently because you regained. You will need to prepare yourself mentally and emotionally for any substantial weight loss that will result in having trouble accepting your new body size.

Phantom fat occurs when you believe you are larger than you actually are. Some aspects of your body size that you need to understand and prepare in advance for are that you may be unhappy with your appearance after losing weight. This occurs because you may be disappointed in where you did or did not lose weight and fear of regaining weight.

Weight regain only occurs when you hang on to your old habits, thoughts, or feelings, and fear that lead to weight gain. You will not regain all of your lost weight when you are dedicated to your daily routine and have consistent support mentally from yourself or others.

Another aspect of your life that radically shifts is your relationships with others. You need to prepare for shifts in your relationship dynamics. By losing weight, others will see you differently. You will receive compliments and extra attention when, in the past, you were ignored. This may cause feelings of discomfort, resentment, or self-consciousness.

Your social activity is also going to change. Not all of your social interactions will be about food because your eating habits will change. You will notice how most of your social activities surround food. With this new awareness, you can decide how you act and interact with others in these organized functions.

You can encourage activities that do not only revolve around food. These can be visiting museums, going for walks, or bringing healthier snacks to a family function as a safe alternative that meets your food goals. You can incorporate more fruits and vegetables to make your time more successful.

To prepare yourself before a social function, you need to have a decent amount of mental preparation. This is important because once you arrive at an event, you can remain focused on achieving your health goals. Before the event and while you are there, you can mentally coach yourself, reconnect back to your bigger goals, and remind yourself what you most desire. Your goals are the reasons for your weight loss journey.

These goals include increasing strength, losing weight, feeling healthy, healing your body, becoming more balanced, and feeling good again. These reminders empower and fuel your healthy choices to make it easier to resist any possible temptations.

After your social gathering, you can celebrate your dedication instead of feeling negative or impulsively reacting.

Other healthy suggestions when you are at a social gathering is forgoing alcoholic beverages and choosing non-alcoholic drinks as a healthier alternative. Alcohol dehydrates you and lowers your ability to make rational decisions. This will make your commitment to your goals more challenging.

Your mental preparation is a great start to increasing your social interactions. Using substation and addition as techniques instead of deprivation and starving yourself are great beginning steps.

In Summation:

Choosing to eat healthily is a commitment that is hard when you are doing it alone. Building a strong support network increases your odds of remaining successful long after this program ends. Cultivating daily habits are the necessary foundational blocks on your road to a healthy lifestyle.

Along with building your social community, you will also need to prepare yourself before and during social situations. These may be giving yourself a pep talk to prepare the judgment from family members who do not approve of your choices or friends who are jealous of your different lifestyle.

Understand that putting yourself first is a brave and new concept that your friends and family need to understand. Your weight loss goals are private and have nothing to do with anybody other than you.

Expect these relationships to begin a transformation similar to how you are transforming yourself from the inside out.

Day 19:

Weight loss is a change to your mind and body. You are rewiring how you respond to food. Day 19 of your weight loss program tackles the perspective of sugar and how it causes food addiction. Obesity increases yearly in adults and leads to increases in type II diabetes and heart disease. The origin of these many obesity-related diseases and illnesses links back to sugar. Sugar is present in almost all the food that is ready for you to consume. Your body has relief and becomes accustomed to sugar cravings. Brain scans have confirmed that sugar consumptions affect your brain, similar to certain drugs.

According to the Neuroscience & Biobehavioral Reviews, they found that sugar is categorized as a substance of abuse that may be addictive to those who binge on it. This occurs because your limbic system is affected by sugar, which controls your emotions. The study found that regular sugar consumption leads to behavioral and chemical changes that resemble the side effects of substance abuse. This study proves that food addiction is real, and sugar is the main component of this addiction.

Obesity is treated as a disease. Similar to alcoholism, obesity is related to genetic, psychological, neurological, and hormonal impairments. Obesity and alcoholism negatively affect social and interpersonal relationships, and unfortunately, you cannot quit eating, but you can stop drinking. This unfortunate fact reveals the difficulty of quitting sugar when it is present in food that you need to survive.

Learning how to control, monitor, and lessen food addiction is essential in treating obesity. The beginning step is monitoring and evaluating the effect sugar has on the body and brain. Popular ways you can ingest sugar is through soft drinks. Sodas are an easy culprit because of their excessive amount of sugar. Other sources of increased sugar content are through packaged or processed foods. Sugar is a common ingredient in many foods that you may assume to be healthy.

When you eat sugar, your brain releases a surge of dopamine. Dopamine is the source of happiness and pleasure. Eating sugar has a similar reaction in the brain as heroin and cocaine. Your brain perceives sugar as beneficial and positive, which can mimic the effects of addiction through large cravings for sugar.

When you cut out sugar from your diet, you will have withdrawal symptoms. This is why, during weight loss, it is often difficult and challenging to resist sweets like candy and cake when you have become used to their effect on your brain. You are rewarded with feelings of happiness, and going without that feeling is uncomfortable.

During your four-week weight loss program, you will have an intense withdrawal from sugar if your diet consistently and regularly consists of high-fructose corn syrup. The goal of this program is to cultivate new healthier habits, which will gradually decrease your need and desire for sugary products.

You will need to practice compassion during this process. Shaming yourself as your body adjusts to a new normal is not beneficial and makes the process harder to adapt to.

As you progress with your weight loss plan, you may have felt or feel withdrawals from a lack of sugar in your diet in your third week. Quitting sugar cold turkey can lead to fatigue, stomach pains, and headaches. These symptoms indicate withdrawal from a dietary addiction. Whether you're addicted to sugary cookies, cakes, or candy, it's a real and serious concern.

The medical community recognizes the seriousness of the physical symptoms of withdrawal. Withdrawal symptoms from drugs, alcohol, and caffeine are real and dangerous. Eliminating sugar from your diet can lead to many withdrawal symptoms and be challenging to adapt to.

Refined sugar and processed carbohydrates affect the brain similarly to drugs and alcohol. This indicates that sugar hijacks your brain and creates a food-dependent cycle. This shows why weight loss and regaining weight is so common due to physical pain that many obese adults are unable to sustain long-term weight loss.

Some alternative foods that help curb your sugar cravings are eating healthy fats such as nuts, avocados, and olive oil. These helps calm down your sugar withdrawal-like symptoms. Monitor your symptoms closely and write down your reactions in your food journal. If your symptoms do not improve, see your doctor and check if your body is reacting to something related to sugar or not.

Other preventative measures you need to consider when embarking on your weight loss journey is whether or not quitting sugar cold turkey is the right approach. Cutting entire food groups from your diet is adventurous, but the goal is not to deprive but to find the right balance. By gradually cutting down on less healthy foods, you will be able to have the time to adjust and maintain your new habits.

You are still able to indulge in some sweet foods and the slower changes you can adapt to more easily. You can also visit a dietician to monitor your food plan, along with you personally managing your diet. You may be advised to drink more water, increase your fiber intake, or take a supplement because you may lack vital nutrients in your diet.

Along with planning your new diet, you need to plan how to handle your bouts of cravings. Your cravings are not in your control, but how you respond is in your power. You need to decide how to deal with your cravings. In order to help eliminate or lessen your indulgent behavior, it is advisable to have a supportive system of others with similar health goals. Furthermore, when you feel a desire to eat, never enter your kitchen.

By entering your kitchen, you are putting yourself at risk for overeating on food that will not help you in maintaining your healthy food goals. Do not shame or feel any form of guilt if you do experience regular moments of sadness, tiredness, or irritability during the first two to five days after quitting on junk food.

These symptoms will eventually simmer down after the initial few days. Weaning yourself off of sugar is usually preferred, but it will take longer than quitting immediately. During your first few weeks, you need to regulate your blood sugar levels through balancing your blood sugar levels, your insulin levels, which cause food addiction.

Starting your mornings with foods high in protein, level out your blood sugar, and this will help limit your sugar cravings throughout the day. Other helpful things you can do to limit your cravings is drinking a lot of water and getting adequate sleep. Lifestyle habits, which have been discussed in previous days in your weight loss program, are the foundation for a healthy and sustainable weight loss life.

In Summation:

Food addiction is real because sugar is a dangerous carbohydrate that creates an addictive relationship between you and your brain. Your brain responds to sugar similarly to how your brain responds to heroin and cocaine. This response is identical due to the rush of dopamine.

Dopamine releases happiness and pleasure, thus perpetuating an addictive relationship. This is why adults struggle with losing weight because their brain is conditioned to respond positively to food with large amounts of processed sugar.

When you attempt a healthier lifestyle, your body will respond differently with less sugar. You will experience a form of withdrawal from sugar. Some adults prefer gradually decreasing their consumption while others quit immediately.

It is your choice as to how best your body responds.

In order to help yourself with your cravings, there are many ways to avoid tempting indulgences. You need to mentally prepare for your actions. Decide on a plan of action, so that you do not consume the dangerous product.

Sugar is dangerous to an adult with excessive weight. Sugar makes you reliant, depressed, and unwilling to stay motivated due to its many addictive side effects.

Learning how your body responds to its absence is vital to prepare how you can handle eliminating or greatly reducing the presence of sugar in your life.

Day 20:

On day 20 of your weight loss program, you will identify the difference between punishment and rewarding yourself throughout your weight loss plan. This includes punishing yourself mentally or physically, which is never beneficial. Rewarding yourself can include praising yourself mentally or physically indulging in a treat to celebrate your hard work. It is important to differentiate between the two and know when it is good to use one other than the other.

Motivation varies from person to person, depending on your mental resiliency and determination. If you are not able to stick to your goals consistently, then you may need to invest in a "punishment" mentality to help motivate you instead of positive reinforcement.

Researchers have found that money is a great motivator for adults to improve their performance, but they discovered that punishment is more effective than reward. Punishment provides an incentive to perform well. This perspective applies to your weight loss program because you may find out that you respond better to the thought of having certain privileges taken from you. These privileges may be certain indulgences, specific food options, or socializing with certain people.

Negative feedback may be more effective than positive feedback in modifying bad behavior and habits. If you are struggling at maintaining good healthy food choices and exercising regularly, then punishment might be the best source of motivation.

An app that can motivate you with punishment is Gym Pact. This app either pays you or deducts real money from your account based on completing your scheduled workouts. This app has an 80 percent success rate due to money being extremely motivating. If you are not ready to invest in an official app, then you can use your honor system and put a dollar in a jar every time you hit the snooze button instead of going to the gym.

Be careful of abusing this system and developing an obsessive-compulsive behavior disorder. Do not use food or exercise as punishment. Using them as punishment creates an unhealthy association with the activity, which can discourage you from continuing to stick to your program. You also run the risk of hating specific exercises and developing an eating disorder. Be mindful and aware of the relationship you have with exercise and eating healthy.

You don't have to punish yourself, only if you see that as a beneficial way to get motivated when you've hit a slump. For reinforcement, the reverse can be true. Exercise is a gradual uplifting of your mood because of the rush of endorphins while increasing your heart rate. You will automatically receive positive side reinforcements through increased stamina and the feel of accomplishment. These positive feelings will increase the chance of you completing this exercise routine again.

To build and maximize your workout motivation, you should start by finding an exercise you love. This can be walking, yoga, cycling, swimming, or dancing. Anything that helps you maintain your exercise routine is encouraged. You can also create an exercise club or group of friends, which can increase your motivation with a little healthy competition.

On the opposite end of the spectrum is the rewarding system to motivate weight loss. A rewarding system includes purchasing a blender as a way to invest in your health. This kitchen tool is a great motivator for preparing healthy meals. This meal prep tool is a great tool invaluable in organizing and planning your weekly meals and can also expand your palette with different food choices and possibilities.

Another helpful reward is using a healthy meal delivery service. This can help you maintain your health goals if you are struggling with meal prep. Hello Fresh and Blue Apron are commonly used services that can help you for a week or two when your work schedule gets too busy.

Another reward you can invest in is a cooking class to sharpen your culinary skills. This may be the best time to invest in yourself if you find yourself in a rut on similar based meals that have grown stale. Cooking classes can inspire you to try new, healthy, and fun things. By learning how to cook new types of food and work on your skills, your chances of maintaining your weight loss will improve as you incorporate new aspects into your life that can last longer than your weight loss program.

Another reward is purchasing new exercise clothes. When you are losing weight, you naturally go down in clothing sizes, and treating yourself to new outfits is a great motivator for continuing on your health journey. Exercise clothes are a great option when you are going down in sizes because they are not typically skin tight and have varying types of quality. When you are more comfortable in your size, you will feel better. When you have better confidence, you will want to reward yourself.

Lastly, a final reward once you have reached your weight loss goals is treating yourself to a vacation. This getaway can be in a neighboring town, state, or country that is centered on your health and wellbeing. Spending money on a positive experience brings you long-lasting tools for happiness and success. You can research an active vacation that includes many activities. These activities may include hiking, cycling, which you may have felt scared to try when you were heavier.

If your vacation seems too grandiose, you can invest in a kitchen scale to monitor portions. A food scale is great for measuring your meals and using portion control. All of these are great positive reinforcements that promote and reward your healthy lifestyle. You need to enjoy your changes and how your body is responding.

In Summation:

Weight loss rewards and punishments are varying types of motivators in your weight loss program. Rewards offer a way to recognize your weight loss achievements through self-discipline. You were able to overcome temptations and stressors. Having set goals for yourself allows your mind to occupy itself with the benefits of reaching those goals.

Rewarding yourself through buying a new dress, taking a new cooking class, or going on a weekend vacation allow you to compliment yourself without compromising your health goals.

When you find yourself slipping on the motivation chart, adding a monetary punishment as an incentive to remain committed is also helpful. This form of punishment is a reaction to not going to the gym to work out or snacking too often. You are holding yourself accountable with more strictness.

Day 21:

On Day 21, your primary focus is learning patience with your weight loss trends. Healthy weight loss is not achieved immediately or overnight. Every choice and action you have cultivated daily promote your weight loss routine. Your basic knowledge and practice of your habits every day are essential to sustain your health plan and to continue your weight loss journey. The other important aspect of sustaining your weight loss plan is patience.

You cannot practice your healthy eating and exercise habits unless patience is involved. Patience is necessary because many adults who have struggled with sustaining a diet or exercise routine is due to a lack of willpower and dedication. If you do not see immediate physical results, you may reject all your cultivated research and knowledge and give up on your behaviors.

The mindset of slow and steady wins the race applies to this situation. It is hard to lose more than one to two pounds a week. Suppose you are losing more than that, you are likely losing muscle, which is not what you want for your body. Losing one to two pounds a week shows you are burning fat the healthy way. Also, adopting a crash-like diet to lose weight quickly is not a healthy approach to lose weight. The slower you lose weight, the more time your body adjusts.

Having patience allows you to maintain your daily habits and resist temptations. Many adults who have tried countless diets regain the weight they lost. This also may have happened to you, which is common and understandable. Patience reduces your stress.

Hurrying your weight loss increases stress, which limits your body from burning fat?

Along with retaining fat, you will have increased cravings for fattening foods. These foods trigger an emotional response. Stress is an emotional cue to avoid unpleasant feelings, and practicing patience will limit this encounter of food cravings.

The primary reason why many adults fail to continue their weight loss plan is because of a diet or meal plan stoppage. You choose to ignore what you've learned and then return to your previous eating habits. You reject your knowledge because you don't think it works since you do not see any immediate results. By adopting a new eating plan, you are incorporating all the new knowledge you have taught yourself and guided yourself through.

You have chosen to maintain your weight loss, not the diet. Do not put all of your power into the diet itself; diets such as Weight Watchers, Nutrisystem, or Jenny Craig. All of these diets do not control your work ethic and knowledge about food. It is all your choice about how much and how often you eat.

Another important aspect is remembering to incorporate all forms of nutrients into your diet. Food groups work together to nourish your body, give you strength, and keep you healthy. Every food plan has a balance that promotes a nutrient-focused meal plan.

Your knowledge about your body and what it needs to function best is important and crucial for your weight loss. Do not fall for the latest diet fads or listen to friends who saw a great diet ad in a magazine. Trust that you have all the necessary knowledge to take care of yourself.

The primary reason why many adults are unable to continue their weight loss plan is to stop eating a diet or meal plan. You choose to ignore what you've learned and then go back to previous eating habits. You reject your knowledge because you think it doesn't work because you don't see immediate results.

Along with listening to yourself, you also have to remember to respect your body. Optimal food to nourish your body includes lean meat filled with protein and healthy fruits and vegetables. Making poor food choices deprives your body of its ideal health, and you will eventually overeat because you are not properly nourished. Listen to your body and how it speaks to you; work on not obsessing over a number on a scale. Achieving a realistic and healthy clothing size is a more attainable goal.

The last skill you need to cultivate is for you to have patience with yourself and others. If you don't lose weight quickly, or if your weight loss has slowed down, you lose faith in yourself. The amount of time it takes to lose weight is not a determinable fact. Losing weight is not an exact science, and your body will respond accordingly. Your success goes beyond the food you choose to eat and is connected to how you handle challenges, stress, and adopt new behaviors to compensate.

Turn off the race mentality, then observe and reflect upon what you had learned, changed, and grown from when you started your weight loss journey to the present. You will notice that your relationship with food has evolved and grown. How you think, act and the feelings you have towards food is not the same, and that required extensive amounts of patience.

Tips to continue living patience filled life is learning what makes you feel good, repeat it, and continue repeating it. When you do something that makes you feel like a failure, learn from it, and move on. Focusing on a perceived failure only makes it worse in the long run.

Another useful skill in practicing patience is for you to only focus on the food on your plate. Ignore other people's food choices and opinions on your eating habits. Other people do not know what is in your mind and heart. Your opinion of yourself is the only opinion that truly matters. Work on celebrating your small and big milestones. Every achievement has meaning and is a success.

Remember that weight loss is not a temporary fix. Weight loss is a reaction to a lifestyle change. You will never be cured of your obesity or being overweight. For your lifestyle to remain healthy, you must continue using the skills and strategies you learned to continue losing, maintaining, and sustaining your healthy weight.

Every skill you have learned is a muscle that needs to be exercised for maximum strength and endurance. Your success will be maintained by finding a strategy that works best with your new lifestyle. To escape negativity or self-doubt, you can practice positive self-talk. By being positive, you will be able to destroy your negative thoughts when you have a weak emotional moment.

To enhance your skills, you can practice resisting tempting food to continue building your tolerance. Having a strong mindset improves through practice. Practicing your willpower through having tempting food near you, increases your chances of diminishing the power that food has over your actions. With time and practice, you will be stronger than any food item.

The final practice round is to increase your social interactions where food is the focus. You can only practice how to eat rather than consume your time and energy with others. What others are eating, drinking, or thinking doesn't have to do with you.

Maintaining your health requires patience. Your thoughts, your body, and your actions require cultivating patience in maintaining your health.

In Summation:

In a society where wanting instant results is the way to go, weight loss is not possible. Weight loss is slow and steady to give your body and hormones the time to adjust and adapt to your new size. You are tired of no results, but on average, you can lose one to two pounds in a healthy way. Sometimes the body is slower than a pound a week.

Everyone responds differently to weight loss. There is no guaranteed method of losing weight other than eating a balanced meal plan with regular exercise. If you have reached a plateau, you can increase the challenges to your exercise routine.

Practice positive self-talk to outweigh your concerns and worries about your progress. You are strong and capable of sustaining your weight loss.

Week 4

Day 22:

Congratulations on starting the final week of your weight loss program. By fostering meaningful mental and physical changes, you demonstrate your dedication to your health. Your ambitious desire to change your relationship to food requires constant attention and dedication. Your weight loss is based on slowly decreasing weight and size, but there are many non-scale victories that you can celebrate as well.

Today you will focus on your non-scale victories.

Your little wins can change your mind to see your body image as an instrument rather than an ornament. You 're more than what you look like. Your health is a wide range of aspects of your life. Your mental, physical, emotional, and spiritual aspects are all valuable aspects of your health and life that go beyond a simple number on a scale.

Throughout your weight loss program, it is helpful to reflect and remember all of your small victories that coincide with reaching your weight loss milestones. Having a balanced nutrition plan with regular exercise automatically brightens your mood. Your mood improves through regular exercise due to the increased circulation, core body temperature, and released endorphins. The release of these hormones provides a positive feeling after exercising, which will help you overcome any low mood episodes. When the temperature decreases, your body naturally wants to go into hibernation, but with regular daily exercise, you can combat those low moments.

Another achievement of your health program is that your daily tasks make it easier for you to manage and complete. Slimming down is a common motivation with fitness and weight loss, but the practical progress is a much more powerful incentive to maintain a healthy lifestyle. Everyday tasks that become easier are walking up the stairs to work without needing to take breaks, wresting your dog into a bath, or playing with your kids on the weekends. All of these daily tasks are made easier and more enjoyable as your health improves. All of these tasks are non-scale victories that go unnoticed most of the time.

Along with increased physical stamina with household activities, your energy to keep up with life, which includes both physically and mentally, has increased as well. Changing your eating habits improves your energy throughout the day. By eating food that fuels you forward throughout your day instead of making you feel sluggish indicates that you are self-regulating your blood sugar levels. This is another small victory but makes the largest impact because you have more determination to increase your activity mentally and physically throughout the day, which makes you more present in your own life.

Excessive weight negatively affects your joints, but with meeting your fitness goals, you can reduce a lot of your discomfort. For every extra pound of weight you carry, there are four pounds of added pressure on your knees. This is dangerous to your health, and any weight loss will improve your health and make your body feel relief.

Along with increased energy, mood, and decreased joint pain, you are also increasing your endurance. Regular cardio workouts build muscle, but also improve your body down to cellular level. Each cell has mitochondria, where you receive all of your energy. With regular interval training and other aerobic exercises, you are increasing your ability to store and expel energy. When you age, you lose more energy in your cells, and regular exercise helps replenish your energy.

Another noticeable improvement to your health is mental clarity and sharpness. Exercise provides pathways in your brain to clear and perform better. You are able to pay attention, plan, coordinate, and make decisions faster, and all of these are done with more rationality. Regular exercise boosts your memory, learning, and understanding of information. Most adults with excessive weight struggle with fogginess in their memory, but your cognitive skills will show noticeable improvement as your physical health improves.

The improvement of the relationship between your mind and body are achievements that are not reflected back by the number on the scale. Your memory is a valuable commodity that allows you to increase your presence with yourself and others.

Along with all of your physical and mental achievements made in your life over three weeks, your body has also positively responded to the change in your diet with lessened cravings. Although you may have found the first three weeks challenging with a strong desire for sugar, your body has stopped reacting to sugar. Your relationship to food is improving, and you are cravings for sweets have lessened, which is breaking away from your sugar cycle.

The sugar cycle happens when you eat too much sugar; your pancreas releases extra insulin. Insulin signals your cells to take in and store more glucose. Your blood sugar then drops, which leads to craving more sugar. Copious amounts of sugar lead to weight gain, but with a controlled diet and not emotionally responding to stress with eating, leads to better behavior on your part. This is a wonderful victory to beat the many food cravings that occur when you change your diet.

Another small but large victory with changing your diet, is having a healthier digestion system. Often, when you do not have a balanced diet and eat large amounts of salt and sugar, you experience bloating, constipation, and indigestion. These are all signs that your digestion system is out of place. There are many reasons, overgrowth of bad bacteria, insufficient fiber, or water intake. All of these improve when your diet changes and include lean protein with whole grain and fruits and vegetables. Your body responds better with more regularity.

Along with your improved health, another large victory on the non-measurable achievements is a better sense of your well-being. With your four weeks of intense personal deep dive into your psyche, physical health, and reflection, your well-being has improved. You have assessed how you feel towards food and your reaction to your emotions. Signs your well-being have improved are feeling better for an extended period, which can lead to higher levels of resiliency to stress. You are getting sick less often, feel calmer, and your emotions have balanced.

More often than not, when your food habits are out of control, and your exercise routine is nonexistent, they are side effects of an overall problem. The problem stems from a lack of care for your health and well-being.

In Summation:

These four weeks mental and physical boot camp demands that you dive deep into your past to understand your relationship with food. To understand your relationship, you must remember and acknowledge all your trauma and why food was the chosen form of comfort.

By analyzing and reflecting, you have been able to change your health in a positive direction and form a healthy relationship with your body, which includes how you eat and exercise. Your well-being has improved tremendously over the past three weeks, and as you move through your final week, you will continue to focus on your habits and work through barriers.

Remember to celebrate all of your non-scale victories. These victories allow you to continue on your path because the weight loss will slow down, but your habits and mindset do not.

Day 23:

Day 23 tackles the mental stress that continues with weight loss. You will have daily and weekly struggles that change and evolve through your health journey. The topic you need to focus on is how your mental health has grown over the past three weeks. Think about the choices and behaviors you have made that have positively and negatively changed you.

There will never be a cure for weight loss, but with active awareness and intuition, you will be able to recognize signs and patterns that indicate your present mental and physical state of health. When you lose weight successfully, you focus on your food choices, how much or how little you exercise, and how you think about food.

It is important for you to remember that your expectations create a large amount of stress in your life. Unmet expectations occur when you are not meeting specific weight loss goals. You need to adapt your expectations accordingly and allow your body time to adjust.

Another way to check in with your current mental state is to think about your past few weeks. Reflect on how you have reacted to stressors outside and inside your control. Life does happen, which is completely understandable and how you choose to respond is either helping or hurting your chances at success. Some life events can include your parents getting sick, your spouse becoming depressed, or that you are having serious problems at work. All these are mental obstacles that need to be expected.

When you expect roadblocks to your health, you can anticipate and plan the proper reactions. A way to handle stress in a helpful manner is by learning how to regroup. You improve your ability to regroup by not giving in to your feelings of hopelessness, helplessness, shame, and feelings of defeat. Do not allow these feelings to slip into your mind. It is helpful to have various plans when life becomes chaotic.

Having a plan A, B, and C is useful. Plan A is wonderfully preferred; plan B is okay, while plan C is not great, but acceptable. Your plan A can include a walk outside, listening to a podcast while you clean your house. Plan B can include exercising at your local gym if the weather is not ideal. Plan B is a great alternative to your original plan A of exercising outside, but you remain committed to your plan of exercise. Plan C can include walking up your stairs at home if you can't go to the gym, so by this, you're still making sure exercise is a priority in your routine.

Often when your daily plan goes awry due to unforeseen circumstances, you give up, but to sustain your new healthy life, you must find ways to commit to a goal.

Along with sticking to daily eating and exercising routines, this is also an important moment in time to reflect upon your current relationship with food. Your relationship can include having an emotional connection or attachment to food that you are still struggling with. It is okay not to have mastered all your attachments yet.

This is a good time to think about why you are stuck and not able to move past your thoughts and actions about this particular food.

This could include choosing to have multiple servings of cake every night because you are having a tough emotional moment.

Instead of having a piece of cake, pause, and think about your actions. Think of your feelings and talk to yourself. Ask yourself if you're actually hungry, why you want the cake, and what you're going to accomplish by eating the cake.

Another way to combat emotional attachments to food is to continue to educate yourself and others with proper nutrition and proper resources for mental health. Find books, therapists, and support groups that discuss how certain foods affect your health. Look for books and ways that can answer any lingering questions or refresh your understanding.

Other ways to balance out your mental health is forgiving yourself when there is a slip-up. At times, life can be challenging, and it is okay if you indulge. The problem arises when your indulgences are daily or multiple times a day.

You were previously reminded of non-scale victories, and it is important to remind yourself that your weight on the scale does not determine your self-worth. Your health is an entire process and achievement. Your health is more than what you look like. It is how you feel, move, think, and respond to life around you. Your problems will not all magically disappear when you are suddenly a "thinner" or more "beautiful "version of yourself.

Your weight loss journey is not effective or enjoyable when you are consistently depriving yourself of small victories. To make sure you are properly supported, having a competent, supportive family or group of friends is essential while you continue on this journey.

Along with your non-scale victories, think back to the reason you started this health journey. You need to remember your reason. Think about your goal, how it has evolved, grown, changed, and affected your journey. Your reason can include improving your health, slimming down your body frame, increasing activity in your social or family life.

There is no right or wrong reason for losing weight and starting a health journey.

In Summation:

Day 23 focuses on a mental check-in on where your struggles still reside after weeks on your weight loss program. Some struggles are resisting food cravings and dealing with stress.

Stress comes in many colors and sizes in life. Stress can originate from work, friends, family, or yourself, but learning how to rebound from that stress is critical in maintaining your wellbeing.

Some common side effects of out-of-control stress include frequent bouts of sickness, increased heart rate, headaches, moodiness, and lack of focus. Your well-being is in your control, and regular exercise, as well as eating healthy is a great way to combat stress.

Day 24:

Day 24 discusses the struggles with accepting your past and current body shape. Body image is a topic that many overweight adults struggle with regularly. Obesity is a national epidemic that is increasing yearly. Along with increased cases of obesity are increased cases of troubled self-esteem surrounding body image. Body image relates to how you perceive yourself and your body visually.

Body image can include how you talk and think about yourself and others about your body. For many overweight adults, body image is an extremely sensitive topic to discuss. This may occupy your thoughts more than you wish they would. Overweight people usually feel "othered" because their shape and size are outside the normally considered range of body type and attractiveness. This mentality affects how you think and treat yourself.

Your body image can be influenced by comments from others about how you look. These can be both positive and negative. Other ways your body image is influenced is exposure to media, experiencing discrimination based on your appearance, and how frequently you compare yourself to others.

Ways to combat negative and unhealthy body image thoughts are learning to adopt an appreciative view towards your body. Appreciate your body and what it can accomplish. Think of your body as an instrument that moves with you, rather than an ornament that is only meant to be gazed upon.

Incorporate positive affirmations to shut down negative voices. You can start with, "I am strong and beautiful." This will begin to stop your negative thinking patterns. You are a whole person that is unique and flawed. Practice looking at yourself in the mirror, do not avoid yourself in the mirror, and while you are looking at yourself, repeat your positive affirmations. These are ways your body image will gradually improve because you will start believing in yourself and celebrating your hard work.

Weight loss gradually improves self-esteem. You will gain more confidence with your new size and appreciate your weight loss. As you continue embarking on your weight loss journey, you will improve and increase your exercising, but your emotions will also need as much attention.

Your body image is all how you perceive yourself. This means that even when you do lose weight, you may still see yourself as larger, heavier, shorter, or stockier than you really were. Weight loss does not always create a positive body image. Your body image is an individual journey that takes more than weight loss to overcome any negative perception about yourself.

The best starting point with body image is for you to recognize your own value. You deserve happiness and contentment regardless of your weight and how your body looks. Meditation is a helpful tool in grounding your body and mind, and this also improves your overall well-being. You can also begin a gratitude journal to practice bringing more positivity into your life.

Many overweight adults feel intense, ashamed, and guilty because they have not been able to lose weight permanently. The intense pressure to maintain a specific body type and appearance is stressful for many adults. The fear of regaining weight is real and expected. You do not want to see yourself as a failure, but if you are only looking at the numbers instead of all that you have learned, then you will struggle.

Your journey is based on your choices. Choosing the right food for your body, the right exercise for your mind and body are key steps in changing your health. Your appearance is part of accepting who you are. To improve your self-esteem, you can increase your self-confidence.

Believing that you can lose weight, increases the odds of you losing weight and reaching your weight loss goal. Train your brain to believe in yourself. Believing you are not enough will not magically change when you lose weight. Changing your inner dialogue helps you to continue moving forward.

In Summation:

Body image and self-esteem are interconnected with one another on your weight loss journey. Your body image has been seen by society as a hindrance and worthless, which only promotes an unhealthy mindset and perception of your own body.

To begin finding value in yourself is a great step forward in promoting a healthy mindset towards your self-esteem. This can occur when you start noticing yourself looking different or clothes fitting differently. You may see yourself in a different light when exercising is becoming more natural and comfortable. You might be receiving more attention from others, which can be both positive and negative.

All changes to your health impact your self-esteem, and your mental awareness needs more time to catch up while your actions have moved ahead. Your confidence cannot be manufactured; it has to be believed and acknowledged by you first before you can believe it from anyone else.

To help improve your body image and its relationship to self-esteem, you should see a therapist to help improve your mindset when you think you can't do it on your own.

Day 25:

Day 25 focuses on the characteristics of gratitude, dedication, and discipline for optimal weight loss success. These characteristics are necessary for your weight loss program to move beyond the one-month long program. These characteristics need to be understood, molded and utilized for continued success for the future after you finish your weight loss program.

After almost four weeks of focusing on your health, you may have noticed your commitment levels slipping. Society tells you that you deserve instant gratification, and if you do not get your results in a timely manner, then there is no purpose for your hard work. This is not the right or appropriate mentality for sustained weight loss.

Remembering why you've been devoting your life to weight loss is prolonging your life. By reducing your intake of food, you are slowing down the aging process from the inside out. Choosing to make better food choices is your choice to make an effort to eat better.

Many people are struggling to maintain their weight loss goals. You are worth fighting, and giving your health time and attention is necessary for long-term health. Every day you don't make the right choice about your health, and well-being increases your weight gain, increases your poor health, damages your mind, and negatively affects your family and friends.

Losing weight takes time to learn better lifestyle habits and sacrifice. Creating a healthy lifestyle means doing things you do not always want to do. Your willpower requires focus and determination.

To maintain your motivation for a healthy weight loss, you need to find which eating method works best with your life. Decide whether or not you prefer counting your calories, reducing your portion sizes, reducing your snacks, decreasing fried foods, and desserts, or including more fruits and vegetables to maintain your weight loss.

Along with deciding what food plan works best for you, also keeping a journal that allows you to track your daily food intake and mood levels is helpful in noticing old and new patterns. With weight loss, there may be an increase or decrease in certain moods that will be determined by your diet and exercise patterns. Having a record to reflect back on is helpful in motivating you to continue and improve your diet and exercise plan.

To remain motivated and on the right track, it is helpful to problem-solve and brainstorm potential triggers, challenges, and setbacks. This will keep you from remaining motivated. In order to cope with stress, there are some methods that help, and these methods are exercise, deep breathing exercises, taking a bath, going outside for fresh air, calling a friend and asking or seeking out help.

It is normal to reach a plateau and roadblock in your quest for health and wellness. Knowing when you have reached your personal limit is essential to remaining motivated when you know you need assistance.

Another way to remain committed is by strengthening your habits instead of setting hard goals. You may have become intimated by your goals. Your behavior is largely within your control, and your cultivated habits lead to the outcome you want. Your goal provides directions, but habits and commitment keep you moving forward every day.

Another trait you need to cultivate actively is gratitude. Gratitude is appreciating what you find worthy and meaningful. Gratitude leads to success by increasing your confidence because you realize that you are in control. Your control prevents victimhood mentality and complaining over perceived failures. Gratitude is best used in an emotional way. Stop attacking your body and start advocating and promoting your strengths.

Feeling and expressing gratitude towards yourself starts with appreciating and loving your body. You are not just changing your exercise and eating habits, you are also changing your entire life. You are changing how you see yourself and what you are capable of doing by celebrating your success through acknowledgment.

Starting a practice of gratitude begins with writing a list of why you are grateful to your body. This may include breathing, fighting illness, digesting food, seeing, and hearing. You will learn to celebrate all the gifts your body gives you daily, which is great to motivate your weight loss.

In Summation:

Weight loss is able to survive past barriers and stress in your life through daily practices of discipline, motivation, and gratitude. These three characteristics work well together in helping you to maintain your healthy lifestyle and commitment to yourself.

Gratitude promotes a healthy relationship with food and reduces stress through understanding and noticing your actions in regards to food.

Motivation encourages finding ways to address barriers to your health by planning and preparing alternative ways to achieve your goals. This involves supporting alternatives to exercise and anticipating possible scenarios that could lead to negative behavior and actions.

Discipline entrails acknowledging the daily work you must put into yourself for the reward of a healthy weight and life. You will have to resist certain foods and behaviors in order to maintain a healthy weight, but having that awareness will allow you to continue to feel appreciation for the work you've heard.

Day 26:

Day 26 focuses on how you can learn to enjoy food and understand that food is not the enemy. Food can be celebrated and enjoyable. Practicing gratitude improves your relationship with food because you will learn not to be obsessive about food, but to cherish the experience of eating.

Having your daily thoughts and actions obsessed with weight increases your negative self-image and miserable feelings. Spending all day and everyday thinking about your weight, how you dislike your appearance, and how deprived you are due to your current diet leads to more resistance as you attempt at correcting your behaviors and thought patterns.

Learning to enjoy and appreciate your food is cultivated with an attitude that notices the blessing and gifts your healthy new life provides. Having a grateful mindset leads to feelings of confidence and positive energy because you have mastered the ability to enjoy your cup of tea instead of engaging in disordered eating.

To practice intuitive eating, you can start by thinking back on the last meal you ate. Where you aware of how it tasted, the texture and flavor of the food? Did you appreciate how it nourished you and gave you health and vitality? Did you feel good about eating it?

If you instead swallowed your food and barely noticed the flavor and felt guilty and ashamed for eating, it indicates that you did not enjoy or have gratitude for the food you ate.

Reflecting upon your reactions and interactions to food are important to recognize because how you feel about the food you eat affects your body.

With practice, your confidence grows, and with increased self-confidence, your relationship with food improves as well. You may feel or have felt discouraged because you are not losing weight as quickly as you want or have hit the dreaded plateau, and nothing appears to be happening. This is not the case.

There is always an initial weight loss and a time when the body stops losing weight as it adjusts to its new hormones and chemistry, but eventually, you resume losing weight. Having confidence in yourself will prevent a defeatist attitude because of your gratitude towards your cultivated habits.

When you believe in yourself, you change how your brain operates and functions. You are happier and healthier, and with this, you can enjoy yourself and food. With increased happiness, you become less reactive and less resistant. This promotes a healthy and well-balanced mindset.

When you are craving a sugary doughnut or cookie, you have started an urgent response in your brain that initiates the stress response. When you practice gratitude, you are more willing to wait out your cravings through practiced self-control.

By increasing your ability to wait, you delay the instant gratification response. By viewing food as an enemy that must be avoided, you are depriving your body of essential nutrients that it needs. This mindset needs to shift towards focusing on what goes well for your mind and body when you choose appropriate foods, how much you have learned and grown since starting your health journey and everything you now have.

Reminding yourself of all of the value in your life is key to bridging the gap between complaining and gratitude. Controlling your emotional reactions allows you to change your actions. By having healthy habits controlled and regulated daily, you are better prepared for unplanned stress.

By appreciating the food you choose to have, you can increase your gratitude for the small things. A small noticeable observation is the smell of coffee brewing in the morning or how your spouse smiles at you when you walk through the door or the sound of your child laughing. All of these are small moments that you can and should be aware of and thankful for.

Small moments are similar to the little moments before every meal. Taking the time to observe and practice gratitude for the food you have prepared and will ingest to nourish your body and mind is a healthy perspective to practice.

Overall, your daily willpower and discipline to change and harness your daily routines only survive for so long when you do not have a purpose and are wandering aimlessly. Choosing to appreciate and notice the joy in life, everything you have, and what your loved ones have done for you are the reasons for your continued weight loss.

Be thankful for the love in your life, and return that love back to you.

In Summation:

When you feel good about the food you eat, and you express appreciation and gratitude for it, your emotions are reflected in how your body reacts to what you eat. You can gain weight based on what you feel.

Food does not exist to help you suppress your emotions or avoid boredom. It is not there for you to stuff it down faster than you can taste it.

Food is supposed to be pleasurable. Weight loss is not only about what you eat, but how you feel about food. Feeling gratitude towards the food you eat changes how you feel towards food.

Day 27:

Day 27 focuses on the topic of mindfulness in relation to weight loss. Mindfulness promotes a healthy balance between your mind and body that allows your mind to connect with your feelings and allow positive changes to occur. Meditation is the practice that connects your mind and body to allow serene calmness. Meditation reduces stress and helps improve the relationship between you and your thoughts.

Many overweight adults struggle with positive self-talk and body image. There are many stressors that coincide with weight loss and maintaining a diet plan. Meditation provides the time and space for you to understand yourself and how your mind and body work together and separately. Increasing your awareness helps you understand your eating patterns and present barriers that are still challenges.

Meditation does not allow you to lose weight overnight. With practice and determination, you can incorporate the lasting effects on your behaviors and thought patterns. Mindfulness meditation benefits adults who are struggling with weight loss because this technique is an effective method for losing weight and changing eating habits.

Mindfulness pays close attention to where you are, what you are doing, and how you are feeling in the present moment. You acknowledge all these aspects without judgment and let them flow past your mind.

This is extremely helpful during the beginning stages of a weight loss program because you will experience many troubling moments in maintaining your plan and committing to your goals. Mindfulness encourages forgiveness and letting go of shame and guilt. Mindfulness allows a safe place in your mind where you can recognize your feelings and behaviors.

Here is a specific mindfulness meditation you can start. To begin, you start focusing on your breath, watch as your chest or stomach rises and falls. Feel the air move in and out of your mouth or nose. Listen to the sounds the air makes. Observe for a minute or two until you feel more relaxed.

Next, have your eyes open or closed.

1. Take a deep breath in. Hold for several seconds.

2. Slowly exhale and repeat.

3. Breathe naturally.

4. Observe your breath as it enters your nostrils, raises your chest, or moves your belly.

5. Continue focusing on your breath for 5 to 10 minutes.

6. Your mind will wander; this is normal. Notice and acknowledge your wandering mind and return back to your breath.

7. As you wrap up, reflect on how easily your mind wandered. Acknowledge how easy it was to bring your attention back to your breath.

For other mindfulness techniques for your weight loss, you can incorporate slowing down your meals. This entails chewing slowly and recognizing the taste of each bite. Have a consistent time for eating your meals where you are not multitasking.

Learn to differentiate between hunger and fullness. When you are not hungry, do not eat. If you are full, do not continue to eat. Try to listen to what your body is telling you. Recognize how certain foods make you feel. Pay attention to how you feel after eating certain foods. Which one makes you tired, and which one makes you feel energized.

Practice forgiveness by learning from your actions instead of shaming yourself. Move on from your mistakes. Alongside moving on, make more thoughtful food choices. Spend more time thinking about what you're going to eat before actually eating.

A great starting point in mindfulness is starting with ten minutes every other day and increasing it daily. When you increase your mindfulness, you pay more attention to the subtle cues your body gives that you usually miss when you are distracted.

Chewing each bite thirty times is a great starting point when you eat too quickly. Overall, when you are eating, just focus on eating, and when you are doing other things, do those things.

Other mindful eating techniques are setting your kitchen timer to 20minutes and take that time to eat a normal-sized meal. You can also try eating with your non-dominant hand. Eat silently for five minutes and think about what it took to produce that meal, from the sun's rays to the farmer, to the grocer, then finally the cook. This mindfulness technique also teaches you gratitude for the food process.

Finally, before opening the fridge or cabinet, take a breath and ask yourself if you are really hungry. Do something else like reading or going for a walk to occupy your time.

In Summation:

Mindfulness directs your awareness to the present. It allows you to sleep better, reduces your stress levels, and boosts your energy levels. It also improves your relationship with food. Mindful eating is a real practice that helps shape your relationship with food. It helps you choose healthier foods, lose weight, and enjoy the process of eating.

Mindfulness teaches you to approach eating meals with joy and excitement. Savoring each delicious bite and reveling in the process of nourishing yourself, you are choosing to take care of your body, which is a skill that will serve you for your entire life.

Day 28:

Congratulations on reaching the last day of your final week on your weight loss program. This program has allowed you to confront your past and learn how to manage your present in a healthy way. You were taught how to manage your eating habits and have learned how to incorporate exercise into your daily life. Due to all your hard work, your focus today is on the health goals you have for yourself in the future.

You need to reflect upon your four-week journey and decide whether or not you have reached your initial goal or if you wish to amend it. Throughout this process, you were confronted with your mental barriers and forced to feel some emotions that were not comfortable or easy. Since you allowed yourself to increase your vulnerability, you were able to commit yourself to your new health plan.

To plan for your future after the end of this initial four-week program, you need to reevaluate your goals and decide how to modify them. The main topic covered in this weight loss program is emotional eating. This will reoccur throughout your life as life stressors continuously reenter your life. In these four weeks, you have begun the steps in learning how to recognize your reactions to stress and adapt accordingly.

Some helpful stress antidotes are yoga, meditation, going for a walk, talking to a friend, listening to music, or going to a library. Along with learning about your various emotional states, you also need to practice mindful eating. Mindful eating is essential for sustained weight loss.

The strategy for mindful eating is limiting your distractions and keeping things simple. When you are eating, you need to only focus on eating, and nothing else. Increasing your attention span with food includes eating slowly and patiently.

Maintaining your motivation will be the most challenging aspect of your weight loss journey because the mental anguish that weight loss can lead to disappointment and unresolved feelings of guilt and shame usually reappears. To sustain your weight loss, you need to remain committed to your lifestyle and food choices.

You can remain motivated by having a support system surrounding you that keeps you accountable. Support in the form of friends, family, or an online or in-person support group to encourage you to move past your setbacks. Healthy weight loss is slow and steady, so do not shame yourself when your weight does not immediately come off. If you lose weight too fast, your body and mind will feel drained and sick. You should only lose one to two pounds a week to promote a healthy weight loss.

You will also receive many compliments with your initial weight loss, which helps maintain your motivation to continue, but this eventually levels off. Your changed appearance is no longer fresh and new; why having surface-level goals is hard to maintain. Your goals eventually lose their spark and appeal if they are not based on something more substantial, which would be your overall improved well-being.

To remain motivated, you need to continue tracking your progress. There are many apps you can use to track your goals based on your specific needs. There are fitness trackers or journals that allow you to track the food you eat every day, the calories you burn, the weight you lose, as well as your mood. Seeing your daily results in black and white is a great reminder to hold you to your goal when there is an occasional slip-up.

Along with maintaining your health, your sleep is also vital to your weight loss. When you are sleep deprived, maintaining motivation for weight loss is challenging. When you have a sleep deficit, your appetite increases, which will lead to overeating and reduce weight loss. You'll also lose your ability to feel when you're full, therefore leading you to keep on eating. A great goal is to maintain at least eight hours of sleep at night. This will maintain your dedication and your health.

Many overweight adults struggle with maintaining their weight loss once their goal is reached. It is true that many weight loss plans fail in the long term. The main reason is the restrictive nature of dieting. Dieting is hard to maintain over time. Some simple strategies you can implement daily to maintain your health is staying physically active. Walking daily for thirty minutes maintains your cardiovascular system and reduces stress.

Along with regular exercise, you should also eat breakfast regularly. Eating a healthy protein-infused breakfast boosts your metabolism, which limits your hunger throughout the day. Furthermore, having a protein-related breakfast will also ward off cravings. Another helpful habit is checking your scale regularly. Choosing to weigh weekly or twice a month helps detect small weight gains and notice an uptick in weight. You can also discover patterns or needed changes to your habits.

Checking in with your weight on the scale allows you to hold yourself accountable with raw numbers. These numbers do not indicate your sense of worth or value as a person, but it is an indicator that shows when you are not sticking to your healthy habits.

Another important consideration for maintaining and sustaining weight loss is not to resume your old eating habits after reaching your target weight. In the first place, those eating habits caused your weight gain. Instead of being satisfied with your goal of weight loss, you should continue to challenge yourself with new goals.

This new goal does not have to be related to weight loss strictly, but it will keep your confidence on a level high. Along with challenging yourself, you should also increase your education. This includes taking healthy cooking classes, going to health seminars, or participating in fitness fairs. By surrounding yourself with healthy living reminders that allow your motivation to remain intact.

Along with staying involved and educated about your own health, you can also mentor someone struggling with their weight. By mentoring another person, it requires you to stay current with new research and trends in weight loss tools and recommendations.

Another reminder is that with maintaining a weight loss program, you need to learn how to get yourself back on the wagon. Resiliency is an essential skill that is valuable in life and weight loss. Vacations, holidays, and stressful life situations do happen, which can impede your eating plan. These are understandable and okay facts, but the trick is getting back on course as soon as possible. Your weight loss journey is full of learning, not failure. You are more than capable of moving on from any small or large set back as long as you believe in yourself.

Final Thoughts

Choosing to embark on a weight loss journey is not an easy decision. Weight loss is extremely personal and private, but realizing that you need to change and are willing to embrace the necessary work involved are great starting points. The trick with any weight loss program is to start one. Once you decide to change, all you need to do is learn how to adapt and change your life in a healthier way.

The trick for weight loss is improving your health, and the best way to improve your health is to keep it simple. Simple habits can be learned and used to improve your health. The easiest one to tackle first is your physical health. First, add in more healthy protein, fruits, and vegetables while removing starches and junk food. Then add in regular exercise to increase your blood flow and lessen your stress.

All of these are simple additions and changes you can form in your life. The more challenging aspect of weight loss is learning how to love yourself and who you are. Improving your mental health is a great way to maintain weight loss and often more challenging. When you learn to celebrate your body and acknowledge yourself in the mirror, the more confident and motivated, you will become on your health journey.

Overall, consistency is essential in keeping weight off. Adopting this new way of life may seem overwhelming at first, which is expected, but eventually, your new habits and choices will become your second nature when you are used to them.

Your healthy lifestyle will be effortless, so you will be able to maintain your weight much more easily.

You are brave for starting and completing this program. Do not look back, keep moving forward.

Printed in Great Britain
by Amazon